Copyright © 2019

Reza Nazari & Sam Mest

All inquiries should be addressed to:

info@effortlessMath.com

www.EffortlessMath.com

ISBN-13: 978-1-64612-031-4

ISBN-10: 1-64612-031-0

Published by: Effortless Math Education

www.EffortlessMath.com

W0009078

Description

CLEP College Mathematics Math Preparation Exercise Book provides test takers with an in-depth focus on the math portion of the exam, helping them master the math skills that students find the most troublesome. It is designed to address the needs of CLEP College Mathematics test takers who must have a working knowledge of basic Math.

This comprehensive CLEP College Mathematics Math Workbook contains many exciting and unique features to help you score higher on the CLEP College Mathematics Math test, including:

- Content 100% aligned with the 2019 CLEP College Mathematics test

- Prepared by CLEP College Mathematics Math experts

- Complete coverage of all CLEP College Mathematics Math topics which you will need to ace the test

- Over 2,500 additional CLEP College Mathematics math practice questions with answers

- 2 complete CLEP College Mathematics Math practice tests (featuring new question types) with detailed answers

CLEP College Mathematics Math Preparation Exercise Book is an incredibly useful tool for those CLEP College Mathematics test takers who want to review core content areas, brush-up in math, discover their strengths and weaknesses, and achieve their best scores on the CLEP College Mathematics test.

Contents

Chapter 1:

Fractions and Decimals

Topics that you'll learn in this part:

- ✓ Simplifying Fractions
- ✓ Adding and Subtracting Fractions
- ✓ Multiplying and Dividing Fractions
- ✓ Adding Mixed Numbers
- ✓ Subtract Mixed Numbers
- ✓ Multiplying Mixed Numbers
- ✓ Dividing Mixed Numbers
- ✓ Comparing Decimals
- ✓ Rounding Decimals

- ✓ Adding and Subtracting Decimals
- ✓ Multiplying and Dividing Decimals
- ✓ Converting Between Fractions, Decimals and Mixed Numbers
- ✓ Factoring Numbers
- ✓ Greatest Common Factor
- ✓ Least Common Multiple
- ✓ Divisibility Rules

Simplifying Fractions

✎ *Simplify the fractions.*

1) $\frac{33}{54} =$

2) $\frac{12}{15} =$

3) $\frac{18}{27} =$

4) $\frac{12}{16} =$

5) $\frac{26}{78} =$

6) $\frac{10}{40} =$

7) $\frac{20}{45} =$

8) $\frac{18}{36} =$

9) $\frac{40}{100} =$

10) $\frac{6}{54} =$

11) $\frac{15}{27} =$

12) $\frac{15}{20} =$

13) $\frac{20}{32} =$

14) $\frac{26}{32} =$

15) $\frac{15}{75} =$

16) $\frac{40}{70} =$

17) $\frac{24}{48} =$

18) $\frac{35}{84} =$

19) $\frac{15}{40} =$

20) $\frac{15}{60} =$

21) $\frac{30}{54} =$

✎ *Solve*

22) Which of the following fractions equal to $\frac{4}{5}$? _____

A. $\frac{64}{75}$ B. $\frac{92}{115}$ C. $\frac{60}{85}$ D. $\frac{160}{220}$

23) Which of the following fractions equal to $\frac{3}{7}$? _____

A. $\frac{63}{147}$ B. $\frac{75}{182}$ C. $\frac{54}{140}$ D. $\frac{39}{98}$

24) Which of the following fractions equal to $\frac{7}{15}$? _____

A. $\frac{33}{56}$ B. $\frac{25}{85}$ C. $\frac{42}{90}$ D. $\frac{23}{72}$

Adding and Subtracting Fraction

✎Add fractions.

1) $\frac{3}{5} + \frac{2}{4} =$

4) $\frac{7}{8} + \frac{5}{3} =$

7) $\frac{2}{4} + \frac{2}{7} =$

2) $\frac{2}{7} + \frac{3}{5} =$

5) $\frac{3}{5} + \frac{1}{10} =$

8) $\frac{4}{3} + \frac{1}{4} =$

3) $\frac{2}{7} + \frac{1}{4} =$

6) $\frac{2}{9} + \frac{2}{3} =$

9) $\frac{9}{21} + \frac{3}{7} =$

✎Subtract fractions.

10) $\frac{3}{5} - \frac{1}{5} =$

13) $\frac{5}{8} - \frac{1}{5} =$

16) $\frac{5}{6} - \frac{8}{18} =$

11) $\frac{4}{5} - \frac{3}{6} =$

14) $\frac{4}{5} - \frac{6}{10} =$

17) $\frac{5}{12} - \frac{18}{24} =$

12) $\frac{1}{3} - \frac{1}{6} =$

15) $\frac{12}{20} - \frac{3}{10} =$

18) $\frac{1}{5} - \frac{1}{8} =$

✎Solve.

19) A city worker is painting a stripe down the center of Main Street. Main Street is $\frac{8}{10}$ mile long. The worker painted $\frac{3}{10}$ mile of the street. How much of the street painting is left?

20) From a board 8 feet in length, Tim cut to $2\frac{1}{3}$ foot book shelves. How much of the board remained?

21) While taking inventory at his pastry shop, Eddie realizes that he had $\frac{1}{2}$ of a box of baking powder yesterday, but the supply is now down to $\frac{1}{8}$ of a box. How much more baking powder did Eddie have yesterday?

Multiplying and Dividing Fractions

✍ *Multiply fractions. Then simplify.*

1) $\frac{2}{7} \times \frac{5}{9} =$

2) $\frac{2}{4} \times \frac{3}{7} =$

3) $\frac{1}{2} \times \frac{4}{7} =$

4) $\frac{2}{3} \times \frac{1}{5} =$

5) $\frac{9}{10} \times \frac{2}{3} =$

6) $\frac{5}{7} \times \frac{9}{11} =$

7) $\frac{6}{9} \times \frac{2}{6} =$

8) $\frac{3}{4} \times \frac{2}{5} =$

9) $\frac{4}{7} \times \frac{7}{9} =$

✍ *Divide fractions. Simplify if necessary.*

10) $\frac{1}{9} \div \frac{3}{5} =$

11) $\frac{1}{6} \div \frac{2}{7} =$

12) $\frac{6}{9} \div \frac{7}{9} =$

13) $\frac{12}{9} \div \frac{13}{8} =$

14) $\frac{3}{20} \div \frac{5}{10} =$

15) $\frac{1}{5} \div \frac{3}{2} =$

16) $\frac{4}{6} \div \frac{3}{6} =$

17) $\frac{11}{24} \div \frac{1}{12} =$

18) $\frac{7}{14} \div \frac{3}{9} =$

19) $\frac{35}{14} \div \frac{7}{14} =$

20) $\frac{63}{15} \div \frac{14}{20} =$

21) $\frac{110}{50} \div \frac{11}{20} =$

✍ Solve.

22) Vera is using her phone. Its battery life is down to $\frac{2}{5}$, and it drains another $\frac{1}{9}$ every hour. How many hours will her battery last?

    A. $\frac{25}{9}$ B. $\frac{18}{5}$ C. $\frac{16}{5}$ D. 5

23) A factory uses $\frac{1}{3}$ of a barrel of raisins in each batch of granola bars. Yesterday, the factory used $\frac{2}{3}$ of a barrel of raisins. How many batches of granola bars did the factory make yesterday?

    A. $\frac{1}{3}$ B. $\frac{2}{3}$ C. $\frac{3}{2}$ D. 2

Adding Mixed Numbers

✏️ **Add.**

1) $2\frac{1}{4} + 1\frac{1}{2} =$

2) $3\frac{1}{5} + 2\frac{3}{5} =$

3) $2\frac{2}{7} + 1\frac{1}{7} =$

4) $2\frac{1}{4} + 1\frac{3}{4} =$

5) $2\frac{1}{5} + 4\frac{1}{10} =$

6) $3\frac{2}{5} + 1\frac{3}{5} =$

7) $2\frac{1}{5} + 2\frac{2}{3} =$

8) $3\frac{1}{6} + 5\frac{1}{2} =$

9) $3\frac{3}{7} + 5\frac{4}{7} =$

10) $3 + \frac{1}{3} =$

11) $2\frac{2}{5} + \frac{1}{3} =$

12) $2\frac{1}{3} + 2\frac{1}{9} =$

✏️ **Solve.**

13) A baker used $4\frac{1}{2}$ bags of floor baking cakes and $3\frac{3}{5}$ bags of floor baking cookies. How much floor did he used in all?

A. $10\frac{1}{10}$ B. $8\frac{1}{10}$ C. $\frac{16}{10}$ D. $6\frac{2}{10}$

14) Sam bought $2\frac{1}{2}$ kg of sugar from one shop and $6\frac{2}{3}$ kg of sugar from the other shop. How much sugar did he buy in all?

A. $9\frac{1}{6}$ B. $8\frac{1}{6}$ C. $5\frac{1}{6}$ D. $6\frac{1}{6}$

15) A tank has $82\frac{3}{4}$ liters of water. $24\frac{4}{5}$ liters were used and the tank was filled with another $18\frac{3}{4}$ liters. What is the final volume of water in the tank?

A. $75\frac{1}{10}$ B. $70\frac{7}{10}$ C. $76\frac{7}{10}$ D. $76\frac{1}{10}$

Subtract Mixed Numbers

✏️ **Subtract.**

1) $3\frac{2}{3} - 2\frac{1}{3} =$

2) $8\frac{1}{2} - 3\frac{1}{6} =$

3) $6\frac{1}{5} - 3\frac{4}{5} =$

4) $3\frac{1}{7} - 2\frac{2}{7} =$

5) $4\frac{1}{4} - 2\frac{1}{3} =$

6) $5\frac{1}{2} - 3\frac{1}{6} =$

7) $6\frac{1}{4} - 3\frac{1}{2} =$

8) $2\frac{2}{4} - 2\frac{1}{2} =$

9) $2\frac{7}{8} - 3\frac{2}{5} =$

10) $3\frac{1}{3} - 2\frac{2}{6} =$

11) $8\frac{1}{23} - 3\frac{1}{23} =$

12) $3\frac{1}{4} - \frac{7}{12} =$

✏️ **Solve.**

13) When Frodo smiles, his mouth is $2\frac{3}{4}$ in wide. When he is not smiling, his mouth is only $2\frac{1}{4}$ in wide. How much wider is Frodo's mouth when he is smiling than when he is not smiling?

14) Jack jumped $4\frac{1}{7}$ m in a long jump competition. Shane jumped $3\frac{2}{9}$ m. Who jumped longer and by how many meters?

15) Sharon spent $4\frac{3}{7}$ hours studying math and playing tennis. If she played tennis for $2\frac{1}{2}$ hours, how long did she study?

16) Ed just filled up at the gas station, and now his car fuel gauge reads $\frac{8}{10}$ full. He didn't fill the gas tank. If the gauge of fuel was at $\frac{4}{10}$ when he got to the gas station, what fraction of the tank did he fill at the gas station?

Multiplying Mixed Numbers

✍ *Find each product.*

1) $2\frac{3}{4} \times 1\frac{1}{3} =$

5) $4\frac{3}{7} \times 2\frac{5}{8} =$

9) $4\frac{2}{3} \times \frac{3}{7} =$

2) $2\frac{2}{7} \times 2\frac{4}{5} =$

6) $1\frac{1}{7} \times 2\frac{5}{7} =$

10) $5\frac{3}{5} \times 2\frac{1}{2} =$

3) $9\frac{1}{2} \times 3\frac{1}{3} =$

7) $2\frac{1}{2} \times 3\frac{1}{4} =$

11) $3\frac{1}{5} \times 3\frac{1}{2} =$

4) $3\frac{1}{5} \times 3\frac{1}{3} =$

8) $1\frac{1}{9} \times 3\frac{1}{2} =$

12) $4\frac{1}{3} \times 1\frac{1}{3} =$

✍ *Solve.*

13) Kerry read $\frac{2}{3}$ of her chemistry book containing 420 pages. David read $\frac{3}{4}$ of the same. Who read more pages and by how many pages?

14) Victor's weight was 60 kg. He lost $\frac{1}{10}$ of his weight in 3 months. How much weight did he lost?

15) Alex bought 15 kg sweets on his birthday and distributed $\frac{3}{4}$ of it among his friends. How much sweets did he distribute?

16) Shelly distributed a fraction of a cake among 6 girls. Each girl got $\frac{1}{9}$ part of the cake. What fraction of the cake did she distribute in all?

17) The elephants at the Pike Zoo are fed $\frac{1}{2}$ of a barrel of corn each day. The buffalo are fed $\frac{9}{10}$ as much corn as the elephants. How many barrels of corn are the buffalo fed each day?

Dividing Mixed Numbers

✎ *Find each quotient.*

1) $3\frac{1}{5} \div 2\frac{2}{3} =$

2) $4\frac{2}{7} \div 3\frac{1}{2} =$

3) $3\frac{1}{3} \div 4\frac{2}{7} =$

4) $3\frac{3}{7} \div 7\frac{1}{3} =$

5) $3\frac{3}{4} \div 1\frac{3}{5} =$

6) $2\frac{7}{8} \div 2\frac{2}{7} =$

7) $1\frac{1}{2} \div 1\frac{2}{5} =$

8) $3\frac{1}{3} \div 2\frac{1}{3} =$

9) $7\frac{1}{7} \div 3\frac{4}{7} =$

10) $3\frac{4}{5} \div 6\frac{1}{3} =$

11) $4\frac{2}{7} \div 7\frac{2}{4} =$

12) $3\frac{1}{5} \div 1\frac{2}{10} =$

13) $1\frac{2}{3} \div 3\frac{1}{3} =$

14) $2\frac{1}{4} \div 1\frac{1}{2} =$

15) $10\frac{1}{2} \div 1\frac{2}{3} =$

16) $3\frac{1}{6} \div 4\frac{2}{3} =$

17) $4\frac{1}{8} \div 2\frac{1}{2} =$

18) $2\frac{1}{10} \div 2\frac{3}{5} =$

19) $1\frac{4}{11} \div 1\frac{1}{4} =$

20) $9\frac{1}{2} \div 9\frac{2}{3} =$

21) $8\frac{3}{4} \div 2\frac{2}{5} =$

22) $12\frac{1}{2} \div 9\frac{1}{3} =$

23) $2\frac{1}{8} \div 1\frac{1}{2} =$

24) $1\frac{1}{10} \div 1\frac{3}{5} =$

✎ *Solve.*

25) The product of two numbers is 18. If one number is $8\frac{2}{5}$ find the other number.

26) Ashish cut a 25 m long rope into pieces of $1\frac{2}{3}$ meters each. Find the total number of pieces he cut.

27) The cost of $5\frac{2}{5}$ kg of sugar is $\$101\frac{1}{4}$ find its cost per kg.

28) Ana drinks chocolate milk out of glasses that each hold $\frac{1}{8}$ of a liter. She has $\frac{7}{10}$ of a liter of chocolate milk in her refrigerator. How many glasses of chocolate milk can she pour?

Comparing Decimals

✍ *Write the correct comparison symbol (>, < or =).*

1) $0.632 \square 0.631$

2) $0.75 \square 1$

3) $3.91 \square 4.91$

4) $3.2 \square 3.1$

5) $2.8 \square 2.801$

6) $0.4 \square 0.74$

7) $14.9 \square 1.49$

8) $0.707 \square 0.0707$

9) $1.0001 \square 0.999$

10) $3.655 \square 6.6555$

11) $15.4 \square 14.5$

12) $0.909 \square 0.99$

13) $3.3 \square 3.33$

14) $0.304 \square 0.304$

15) $4.0001 \square 4.001$

16) $3.003 \square 3.3$

17) $2.85 \square 2.88$

18) $0.98 \square 0.908$

19) $2.031 \square 2.0031$

20) $5.97 \square 5.79$

21) $6.302 \square 6.203$

22) $0.075 \square 0.57$

23) $1.04 \square 1.0401$

24) $9.101 \square 9.011$

✍ *Solve.*

25) Write the following decimals in ascending order:

$$5.64, 2.54, 3.05, 0.259 \text{ and } 8.32$$

26) Abril wants a cold drink to take with her to the park. She is choosing between a bottle of sparkling water that contains 502.75 ml and a bottle of plain water that contains 499.793 ml. It is a hot day and Abril wants to bring as much to drink as possible. Which beverage should Abril choose?

Rounding Decimals

✍ *Round each decimal number to the nearest place indicated.*

1) 3.12	7) 3.345	13) 5.863
2) 0.356	8) 10.66	14) 101.03
3) 0.49	9) 44.93	15) 1.53
4) 6.75	10) 7.051	16) 0.351
5) 1.724	11) 12.646	17) 100.45
6) 3.276	12) 7.46	18) 7.77

✍ *Round off the following to the nearest tenths.*

19) 22.652	21) 47.847	23) 16.184
20) 30.342	22) 82.88	24) 71.79

✍ *Round off the following to the nearest hundredths.*

25) 5.439	27) 26.1855	29) 91.448
26) 12.907	28) 48.623	30) 29.354

✍ *Round off the following to the nearest whole number.*

31) 23.18	36) 56.7	41) 6.52
32) 8.6	37) 13.75	42) 12.34
33) 14.45	38) 12.55	43) 50.51
34) 7.5	39) 14.25	44) 31.501
35) 3.95	40) 156	45) 101.16

Adding and Subtracting Decimals

✍️ *Add and subtract decimals.*

1) $\begin{array}{r} 17.81 \\ -\ 10.38 \\ \hline \end{array}$

2) $\begin{array}{r} 37.03 \\ -\ 15.9 \\ \hline \end{array}$

3) $\begin{array}{r} 64.12 \\ -\ 33.33 \\ \hline \end{array}$

4) $\begin{array}{r} 14.58 \\ +15.03 \\ \hline \end{array}$

5) $\begin{array}{r} 17.96 \\ +\ 10.01 \\ \hline \end{array}$

6) $\begin{array}{r} 43.02 \\ +\ 71.08 \\ \hline \end{array}$

7) $\begin{array}{r} 93.09 \\ -\ 66.18 \\ \hline \end{array}$

8) $\begin{array}{r} 76.36 \\ -\ 52.60 \\ \hline \end{array}$

9) $\begin{array}{r} 98.45 \\ +\ 45.56 \\ \hline \end{array}$

10) $\begin{array}{r} 12.5 \\ +11.11 \\ \hline \end{array}$

11) $\begin{array}{r} 34.02 \\ -\ 39.00 \\ \hline \end{array}$

12) $\begin{array}{r} 17.56 \\ +\ 13.98 \\ \hline \end{array}$

✍️ *Solve.*

13) $3.56 + \square = 14.7$

14) $\square + 3.5 = 10.6$

15) $12.46 + \square = 17.18$

16) $\square + 6.39 = 10.8$

17) $\square + 3.25 = 5$

18) $14.2 + \square = 17.85$

✍️ *Solve.*

19) Henry weighed two colored metal balls during a science class. The yellow ball weighed 0.88 pounds and the green ball weighed 0.47 pounds. If Henry places both balls on the scale at the same time, what will the scale read?

20) Scarlett has a piece of brown ribbon that is 3.41 inches long and a piece of orange ribbon that is 2.22inches long. How much longer is the brown ribbon?

21) Kate had $368.29. Her mother gave her $253.46 and her sister gave her $57.39. How much money does she has now?

Multiplying and Dividing Decimals

🔸 *Find each product.*

1) $\begin{array}{r} 6.5 \\ \times\ 3.3 \\ \hline \end{array}$

2) $\begin{array}{r} 4.7 \\ \times\ 7.4 \\ \hline \end{array}$

3) $\begin{array}{r} 0.99 \\ \times\ 1.85 \\ \hline \end{array}$

4) $\begin{array}{r} 71.5 \\ \times\ 0.55 \\ \hline \end{array}$

5) $\begin{array}{r} 33.1 \\ \times\ 3.75 \\ \hline \end{array}$

6) $\begin{array}{r} 44.3 \\ \times\ 3.31 \\ \hline \end{array}$

7) $\begin{array}{r} 47.3 \\ \times\ 14.9 \\ \hline \end{array}$

8) $\begin{array}{r} 15.6 \\ \times\ 14.1 \\ \hline \end{array}$

9) $\begin{array}{r} 3.75 \\ \times\ 5.41 \\ \hline \end{array}$

🔸 *Solve.*

10) A hose in a dessert factory pumps out 9.8 liters of chocolate syrup each minute. How many liters of chocolate syrup will the hose pump out in 8 minutes?

11) Diana has a set of wooden boards. Each board is 5.3 meters long. If Diana lays 8 boards end-to-end, how many meters long will the line of boards be?

🔸 *Find each quotient.*

12) $19.5 \div 6.2 =$

13) $45.1 \div 5.5 =$

14) $35.5 \div 10.5 =$

15) $12.5 \div 3.2 =$

16) $17.7 \div 10.3 =$

17) $19.9 \div 20.1 =$

18) $33.8 \div 9.3 =$

19) $71.1 \div 25.3 =$

20) $50.3 \div 40.1 =$

🔸 *Solve.*

21) A factory used 96.7 kilograms of tomatoes to make 4 batches of pasta sauce. What quantity of tomatoes did the factory put in each batch?

Converting Between Fractions, Decimals and Mixed Numbers

✎ Convert fractions to decimals.

1) $\frac{7}{10} =$

2) $\frac{15}{25} =$

3) $\frac{6}{18} =$

4) $\frac{3}{8} =$

5) $\frac{12}{48} =$

6) $\frac{21}{7} =$

7) $\frac{35}{10} =$

8) $\frac{75}{15} =$

9) $\frac{66}{10} =$

✎ Solve.

10) Maria and Darcy are in the same math class. Maria has completed $\frac{2}{3}$ of her math homework. Darcy has completed $\frac{5}{6}$ of her math homework. Which girl has completed more of her math homework?

11) For track practice, runners were supposed to walk or jog twenty laps. Sara jogged $\frac{3}{4}$ of the laps. Jacob jogged $\frac{3}{5}$ of the laps. Sierra jogged $\frac{1}{2}$ of the laps. List the runners in order from least to greatest number of laps jogged.

12) At a sports banquet, Garrett ate $\frac{5}{6}$ of a pizza. Massey ate $1\frac{1}{3}$ of a pizza. Jaime ate $\frac{1}{2}$ of a pizza. List the students in order from who ate the least to who ate the most.

✎ Convert decimal into fraction or mixed numbers.

13) 0.7

14) 0.25

15) 4.3

16) 9.25

17) 4.7

18) 15.5

Factoring Numbers

✎ *List all positive factors of each number.*

1) 35	12) 58	23) 35
2) 17	13) 76	24) 8
3) 42	14) 48	25) 5
4) 24	15) 14	26) 4
5) 33	16) 12	27) 36
6) 22	17) 18	28) 42
7) 39	18) 20	29) 56
8) 51	19) 24	30) 63
9) 34	20) 72	31) 80
10) 18	21) 85	32) 95
11) 69	22) 38	33) 102

✎ *List the prime factorization for each number.*

34) 30	43) 48	52) 12
35) 56	44) 58	53) 18
36) 78	45) 36	54) 24
37) 25	46) 124	55) 55
38) 46	47) 90	56) 75
39) 28	48) 69	57) 9
40) 63	49) 72	58) 10
41) 52	50) 85	59) 15
42) 18	51) 21	60) 14

Greatest Common Factor

✎ *Find the GCF for each number pair.*

1) 36,12	6) 14,42	11) 17,34
2) 18,34	7) 15,80	12) 54,14
3) 25,55	8) 10,35	13) 39,24
4) 18,48	9) 70,30	14) 30,65
5) 21,90	10) 28,36	15) 72,20

✎ *Solve.*

16) Sara has 16 red flowers and 24 yellow flowers. She wants to make a bouquet with the same of each color flower in each bouquet. What is the greatest number of bouquets she can make?

17) At a concert, the band has 8 men's T-shirts and 16 women's T-shirts. The band wants to set up tables to sell the shirts, with an equal number of men's and women's shirts available at each table and no shirts left over. What is the greatest number of tables the band can sell shirts from?

18) Nancy is planting 6 bushes and 15 trees in rows. If she wants all the rows to be the same, with no plants left over, what is the greatest number of rows Nancy can plant?

19) Peter has 12 dollars in his pocket and James has 15 dollars. They want to give money to each other. How much money will they have left after they give to each other the same but highest possible amount?

Least Common Multiple

✐ *Find the LCM for each number pair.*

1) 25,10	8) 51,57	15) 22,10,2
2) 36,18	9) 20,15,10	16) 12,4,16
3) 8,10	10) 12,20,28	17) 9,21
4) 12,18	11) 15,75	18) 25,15,20
5) 24,32	12) 10,25	19) 70,10
6) 14,10	13) 9,7	20) 12,18,24
7) 8,28	14) 78,6	21) 15,45,30

✐ *Solve.*

22) Becky is packing equal quantities of pretzels and crackers for snacks. Becky bags the pretzels in groups of 4 and the crackers in groups of 18. What is the smallest number of crackers that she can pack?

23) Sam and Carlos are bowling with plastic pins in Sam's living room. Remarkably, Sam knocks down 8 pins on every bowl, and Carlos knocks down 9 pins on every bowl. At the end of the day, Sam and Carlos have knocked down the same total number of pins. What is the least number of total pins that Sam and Carlos could have each knocked down?

24) Regan's Bakery sells muffins in packages of 9 and cookies in packages of 11. Going through yesterday's receipts, a store manager notices that the bakery sold the same number of muffins and cookies yesterday afternoon. What is the smallest number of muffins that the bakery could have sold?

Answers of Worksheets

Simplifying Fractions

1) $\frac{11}{18}$

2) $\frac{4}{5}$

3) $\frac{2}{3}$

4) $\frac{3}{4}$

5) $\frac{1}{3}$

6) $\frac{1}{4}$

7) $\frac{4}{9}$

8) $\frac{1}{2}$

9) $\frac{2}{5}$

10) $\frac{1}{9}$

11) $\frac{5}{9}$

12) $\frac{3}{4}$

13) $\frac{5}{8}$

14) $\frac{13}{16}$

15) $\frac{1}{5}$

16) $\frac{4}{7}$

17) $\frac{1}{2}$

18) $\frac{5}{12}$

19) $\frac{3}{8}$

20) $\frac{1}{4}$

21) $\frac{5}{9}$

22) B

23) A

24) C

Adding and Subtracting Fractions

1) $\frac{11}{10}$

2) $\frac{31}{35}$

3) $\frac{15}{28}$

4) $\frac{61}{24}$

5) $\frac{7}{10}$

6) $\frac{8}{9}$

7) $\frac{11}{14}$

8) $\frac{19}{12}$

9) $\frac{18}{21}$

10) $\frac{2}{5}$

11) $\frac{3}{10}$

12) $\frac{1}{6}$

13) $\frac{17}{40}$

14) $\frac{1}{5}$

15) $\frac{3}{10}$

16) $\frac{7}{18}$

17) $-\frac{1}{3}$

18) $\frac{3}{40}$

19) $\frac{1}{2}$

20) $5\frac{2}{3}$

21) $\frac{3}{8}$

Multiplying and Dividing Fractions

1) $\frac{10}{63}$

2) $\frac{3}{14}$

3) $\frac{2}{7}$

4) $\frac{2}{15}$

5) $\frac{3}{5}$

6) $\frac{45}{77}$

7) $\frac{2}{9}$

8) $\frac{3}{10}$

9) $\frac{4}{9}$

10) $\frac{5}{27}$

11) $\frac{7}{12}$

12) $\frac{6}{7}$

13) $\frac{32}{39}$

14) $\frac{3}{10}$

15) $\frac{2}{15}$

16) $\frac{4}{3}$

17) $\frac{11}{2}$

18) $\frac{3}{2}$

19) 5

20) 6

21) 4

22) $\frac{18}{5}$

23) 2

Adding Mixed Numbers

1) $3\frac{3}{4}$

2) $5\frac{4}{5}$

3) $3\frac{3}{7}$

4) 4

5) $6\frac{3}{10}$

6) 5

7) $4\frac{13}{15}$

8) $8\frac{2}{3}$

9) 9

10) $3\frac{1}{3}$

11) $2\frac{11}{15}$

12) $4\frac{4}{9}$

13) $8\frac{1}{10}$

14) $9\frac{1}{6}$

15) $76\frac{7}{10}$

Subtract Mixed Numbers

1) $1\frac{1}{3}$

2) $5\frac{1}{3}$

3) $2\frac{2}{5}$

4) $\frac{6}{7}$

5) $1\frac{11}{12}$

6) $2\frac{1}{3}$

7) $2\frac{3}{4}$

8) 0

9) $-\frac{21}{40}$

10) 1

11) 5

12) $2\frac{2}{3}$

13) $\frac{1}{2}$

14) $\frac{58}{63}$, Jack

15) $1\frac{13}{14}$

16) $\frac{2}{5}$

Multiplying Mixed Numbers

1) $3\frac{2}{3}$

2) $6\frac{2}{5}$

3) $31\frac{2}{3}$

4) $10\frac{2}{3}$

5) $11\frac{5}{8}$

6) $21\frac{5}{7}$

7) $8\frac{1}{8}$

8) $3\frac{8}{9}$

9) 2

10) 14

11) $11\frac{1}{5}$

12) $5\frac{7}{9}$

13) David, 315 pages

14) 6kg

15) $11\frac{1}{4}$

16) $\frac{6}{9}$

17) $\frac{9}{20}$

Dividing Mixed Numbers

1) $1\frac{1}{5}$

2) $1\frac{11}{49}$

3) $\frac{7}{9}$

4) $\frac{36}{77}$

5) $2\frac{11}{32}$

6) $1\frac{33}{128}$

7) $1\frac{1}{14}$

8) $1\frac{3}{7}$

9) 2

10) $\frac{3}{5}$

11) $\frac{4}{7}$

12) $2\frac{2}{3}$

13) $\frac{1}{2}$

14) $1\frac{1}{2}$

15) $6\frac{3}{10}$

16) $\frac{19}{28}$

17) $1\frac{13}{20}$

18) $\frac{21}{26}$

19) $1\frac{1}{11}$

20) $\frac{57}{58}$

21) $3\frac{31}{48}$

22) $1\frac{19}{56}$

23) $1\frac{5}{12}$

24) $\frac{11}{16}$

25) $2\frac{1}{7}$

26) 15

27) $18\frac{3}{4}$

28) $5\frac{3}{5}$

Comparing Decimals

1) $0.632 > 0.631$
2) $0.75 < 1$
3) $3.91 < 4.91$
4) $3.2 > 3.1$
5) $2.8 < 2.801$
6) $0.47 < 0.74$
7) $14.9 > 1.49$
8) $0.707 > 0.0707$
9) $1.01 > 0.999$

10) $3.655 < 6.6555$
11) $15.4 > 14.5$
12) $0.909 < 0.99$
13) $3.3 < 3.33$
14) $0.304 = 0.304$
15) $4.0001 < 4.001$
16) $3.003 < 3.3$
17) $2.85 < 2.88$
18) $0.98 > 0.908$

19) $2.031 > 2.0031$
20) $5.97 > 5.79$
21) $6.302 > 6.203$
22) $0.075 < 0.57$
23) $1.04 < 1.0401$
24) $9.101 > 9.011$
25) 0.259, 2.54, 3.05, 5.46, 8.32
26) sparkling water

Rounding Decimals

1) 3.1
2) 0.36
3) 0.5
4) 7
5) 1.72
6) 3.28
7) 3.3
8) 11
9) 45
10) 7.1
11) 12.65
12) 7

13) 5.9
14) 101
15) 2
16) 0.4
17) 100
18) 8
19) 22.7
20) 30.3
21) 47.9
22) 82.9
23) 16.2
24) 71.8

25) 5.44
26) 12.91
27) 26.19
28) 48.62
29) 91.45
30) 29.35
31) 23
32) 9
33) 14
34) 8
35) 4
36) 57

37) 14
38) 13
39) 14
40) 156
41) 7
42) 12
43) 51
44) 32
45) 101

Adding and Subtracting Decimals

1) 7.43
2) 21.13
3) 30.79
4) 29.61
5) 27.97

6) 114.1
7) 26.91
8) 23.76
9) 144.01
10) 23.61

11) -4.98
12) 31.54
13) 11.14
14) 7.1
15) 4.72

16) 4.41
17) 1.75
18) 3.65
19) 1.35
20) 1.19

21) $679.14

Multiplying and Dividing Decimals

1) 21.45	7) 704.77	13) 8.2	19) 2.81
2) 34.78	8) 219.96	14) 3.38	20) 1.25
3) 1.8315	9) 20.2875	15) 3.9	21) 24.175
4) 39.325	10) 78.4	16) 1.71	
5) 124.125	11) 42.4	17) 0.99	
6) 146.633	12) 3.14	18) 3.63	

Converting Between Fractions, Decimals and Mixed Numbers

1) 0.7

2) 0.6

3) 0.33

4) 0.375

5) 0.25

6) 3

7) 3.5

8) 5

9) 6.6

10) Darcy, 0.833 ...

11) Sierra(0.5), Jacob(0.6), Sara(0.75)

12) James(0.5), Garret(0.833), Massey(1.33)

13) $\frac{7}{10}$

14) $\frac{1}{4}$

15) $4\frac{3}{10}$

16) $9\frac{25}{100}$

17) $4\frac{7}{10}$

18) $15\frac{5}{10}$

Factoring Numbers

1) 1,5,7,35	8) 1,3,17,51	15) 1,2,7,14
2) 1,17	9) 1,2,17,34	16) 1,2,3,4,6,12
3) 1,2,3,6,7,14,21,42	10) 1,2,3,6,9,18	17) 1,2,3,4,6,9,18
4) 1,2,3,4,6,8,12,24	11) 1,3,23,69	18) 1,2,4,5,10,20
5) 1,3,11,33	12) 1,2,29,58	19) 1,2,3,4,6,8,12,24
6) 1,2,11,22	13) 1,2,4,19,38,76	20) 1,2,3,4,6,8,12,18,24,36,72
7) 1,3,13,39	14) 1,2,3,4,6,8,12,16,24,48	21) 1,5,17,85

22) 1,2,19,38

23) 1,5,7,35

24) 1,2,4,8

25) 1,5

26) 1,2,4

27) 1,2,3,4,6,9,12,18,36

28) 1,2,3,6,7,14,21,42

29) 1,2,4,7,8,14,28,56

30) 1,3,7,9,21,63

31) 1,2,4,5,8,10,16,20,40,80

32) 1,5,19,95

33) 1,2,3,6,17,34,51,102

34) $2 \times 3 \times 5$

35) $2 \times 2 \times 2 \times 7$

36) $2 \times 3 \times 13$

37) 5×5

38) 2×23

39) $2 \times 2 \times 7$

40) $3 \times 3 \times 7$

41) $2 \times 2 \times 13$

42) $2 \times 3 \times 3$

43) $2 \times 2 \times 2 \times 2 \times 3$

44) 2×29

45) $2 \times 2 \times 3 \times 3$

46) $2 \times 2 \times 31$

47) $2 \times 5 \times 9$

48) 3×23

49) $2 \times 2 \times 2 \times 3 \times 3$

50) 5×17

51) 3×7

52) $2 \times 3 \times 4$

53) $2 \times 3 \times 3$

54) $2 \times 2 \times 2 \times 3$

55) 5×11

56) $3 \times 5 \times 5$

57) 3×3

58) 2×5

59) 3×5

60) 2×7

61) $2 \times 3 \times 3$

62) 19

63) $2 \times 2 \times 5$

Greatest Common Factor

1) 12

2) 2

3) 5

4) 6

5) 3

6) 14

7) 5

8) 5

9) 10

10) 4

11) 17

12) 2

13) 3

14) 5

15) 4

16) 8

17) 8

18) 3

19) 3

Least Common Multiple

1) 50

2) 36

3) 40

4) 36

5) 96

6) 70

7) 56

8) 969

9) 60

10) 420

11) 75

12) 50

13) 63

14) 78

15) 110

16) 48

17) 63

18) 300

19) 70

20) 72

21) 90

22) 36

23) 72

24) 99

Chapter 2:

Real Numbers and Integers

Topics that you'll learn in this part:

✓ Adding and Subtracting Integers

✓ Multiplying and Dividing Integers

✓ Ordering Integers and Numbers

✓ Arrange and Order, Comparing Integers

✓ Order of Operations

✓ Mixed Integer Computations

✓ Integers and Absolute Value

Adding and Subtracting Integers

✍ *Find the sum.*

1) $(-37) + (-8) =$

2) $8 + (-17) =$

3) $(-53) + (-7) =$

4) $(-41) + (23) =$

5) $(-14) + (-5) =$

6) $(-72) + (-30) + 2 =$

7) $4 + (-40) + (-15) + (-21) =$

8) $91 + (-143) + (-45) =$

9) $(-33) + (-18) =$

10) $(-14) + (58 - 44) =$

✍ *Find the difference.*

11) $(-34) - (-28) - 4 =$

12) $54 - (-12) =$

13) $(-35) - (-5) =$

14) $(-51) - (-34) =$

15) $(-45) - (-30) =$

16) $(-15) - (-10) =$

17) $(-30) - (-14) - (-17) =$

18) $(-10) - (-10) - (-3) =$

19) $(-45) - (-17) =$

20) $(-7) - (-34) - 17 =$

✍ *Solve.*

21) The leaderboard at the Stamford Golf Tournament shows that Nancy's score is 5 and Doug's score is (-1). How many more strokes did Nancy take than Doug?

22) Bridget carefully tracks her money. Her records indicate she spent $300 on a hammock and deposited $1,000 she made from an online auction. Which integer represents the change in how much money Bridget had?

Multiplying and Dividing Integers

✎ Find each product.

1) $(-11) \times (-5) =$

2) $34 \times (-2) =$

3) $(-4) \times 5 =$

4) $7 \times (-10) =$

5) $(-11) \times (-2) \times 2 =$

6) $6 \times (-15) =$

7) $14 \times (-14) =$

8) $(-13) \times (-10) =$

9) $(-14) \times (-4) \times (-5) =$

10) $14 \times (-5) =$

✎ Find each quotient.

11) $210 \div (-14) =$

12) $(-208) \div (-13) =$

13) $(108) \div (-9) =$

14) $(-161) \div (-23) =$

15) $84 \div (-14) =$

16) $(-484) \div (-22) =$

17) $(-162) \div (-18) =$

18) $198 \div 6 =$

✎ Solve.

19) Adam is scuba diving. He descends 5 feet. He descends the same distance 4 more times. What integer represents Adam's new DISTANCE from sea level?

20) The price of jeans was reduced $6 per week for 7 weeks. By how much did the price of the jeans change over the 7 weeks?

21) Yesterday's low temperature was (-2°C). Today's low temperature is 3 times as low as yesterday's low temperature. What is today's low temperature?

Ordering Integers and Numbers

Order each set of integers from least to greatest.

1) $36, -10, 0, 17, 2, -12$ ___ , ___ , ___ , ___ , ___ , ___

2) $43, 10, 21, -30, -1, -12, 2$ ___ , ___ , ___ , ___ , ___ , ___

3) $45, -10, 14, -14, 0, -3$ ___ , ___ , ___ , ___ , ___ , ___

4) $-100, 0, 100, 10$ ___ , ___ , ___ , ___ , ___ , ___

5) $56, -2, -3, -50$ ___ , ___ , ___ , ___ , ___ , ___

6) $18, -6, 15, -1, -10$ ___ , ___ , ___ , ___ , ___ , ___

7) $-20, 12, 0, 15, -30, -2$ ___ , ___ , ___ , ___ , ___ , ___

8) $50, 12, -52, -12, -3$ ___ , ___ , ___ , ___ , ___ , ___

9) $-9, -1, 0, 2, 3, -6$ ___ , ___ , ___ , ___ , ___ , ___

10) $12, 21, -14, 8, -9, 10$ ___ , ___ , ___ , ___ , ___ , ___

Order each set of integers from greatest to least.

11) $-99, 7, 10, 0$ ___ , ___ , ___ , ___ , ___ , ___

12) $5, -4, -2, 0, 10$ ___ , ___ , ___ , ___ , ___ , ___

13) $-30, -100, 33, -33$ ___ , ___ , ___ , ___ , ___ , ___

14) $-81, 10, 71, 23, 51, 12, -3$ ___ , ___ , ___ , ___ , ___ , ___

15) $-3, -2, 6, -32, 5, 12$ ___ , ___ , ___ , ___ , ___ , ___

16) $13, -1, 1, 0, -13$ ___ , ___ , ___ , ___ , ___ , ___

17) $79, 0, 12, -100$ ___ , ___ , ___ , ___ , ___ , ___

18) $99, -1, 23, -3, 0$ ___ , ___ , ___ , ___ , ___ , ___

19) $44, -6, -100, 19$ ___ , ___ , ___ , ___ , ___ , ___

Arrange, Order, and Comparing Integers

✍ Arrange these integers in descending order.

1) $34, 15, -3, -4$ ___, ___, ___, ___, ___, ___

2) $17, -10, 0, -14$ ___, ___, ___, ___, ___, ___

3) $15, -78, -15, -1$ ___, ___, ___, ___, ___, ___

4) $35, -17, 12, -45$.   ___, ___, ___, ___, ___, ___

5) $-30, -10, 71, -15, -14$ ___, ___, ___, ___, ___, ___

6) $62, -20, 12, 15, 14, 0$ ___, ___, ___, ___, ___, ___

7) $-369, 12, -1, 1, 0, -95$ ___, ___, ___, ___, ___, ___

8) $62, -41, -1, 3, 14, 7, -7$ ___, ___, ___, ___, ___, ___

9) $36, -100, 100, -5, 5$ ___, ___, ___, ___, ___, ___

10) $99, -87, 56, -45, -110$ ___, ___, ___, ___, ___, ___

✍ Compare. Use >, =, <

11) $-15 \square 12 =$

12) $-33 \square -16 =$

13) $-65 \square 0 =$

14) $30 \quad -35 =$

15) $96 \quad -96 =$

16) $-568 \square -658 =$

17) $-321 \square -321 =$

18) $545 \square -545 =$

19) $-1000 \square -965 =$

20) $-25 \square -656 =$

21) $-89 \square -100 =$

22) $0 \square -1 =$

23) $10 \square -11 =$

24) $79 \square -100 =$

25) $95 \quad 89 =$

26) $0.2 \square -0.2 =$

27) $12 \square -15 =$

28) $9 \square -9 =$

Order of Operations

✍️ *Evaluate each expression.*

1) $15 + \left(\dfrac{66}{12-((-5)\times 2)}\right) =$

2) $\dfrac{(-55)}{5} + 10 =$

3) $(-13) + (6 \div 2) =$

4) $\dfrac{45}{(-15)} + (3 \times 2) =$

5) $(-40) + (6 \times (-7)) =$

6) $\left(5 \times (-7)\right) - \dfrac{40}{8} =$

7) $(-78) - \dfrac{28}{(-2)} =$

8) $\dfrac{(-80)}{(-4)} =$

9) $15 - \left(3 \times (-7)\right) =$

10) $45 + \left(3 \times (-15)\right) =$

11) $45 - \left(\dfrac{3\times 10}{4+(-2)}\right) =$

12) $(-48) - \dfrac{8}{2} =$

13) $\dfrac{(-35)}{7} + 3 =$

14) $\left(\dfrac{70}{(-14)}\right) - (2 \times 3) =$

15) $36 + ((-2) \times 3) =$

16) $15 - \dfrac{30}{(-6)} =$

17) $78 + (-13) =$

18) $6 + \dfrac{(-51)}{(-17)} =$

19) $5 - \dfrac{25}{-10} =$

20) $\dfrac{3(15-8)}{7} + 5 =$

21) $\left(\dfrac{25-13}{2(3)} - 7\right) \times 2 =$

22) $5 \times \left(\dfrac{55}{11}\right) + 8 =$

23) $(-12) \times \dfrac{48}{6} + 12 =$

24) $\dfrac{96}{-12} - 6 =$

25) $\dfrac{(33\times 2)}{(-6)\times 11} + 1 =$

26) $12 \times \left(\dfrac{45}{(-5)}\right) =$

✍️ *Solve.*

27) Sylvia bought 6 bananas for 60 cents each and 1 apple for 90 cents. Write a numerical expression to represent this situation and then find the total cost in dollar.

Mixed Integer Computations

✍️ *Compute.*

1) $(-70) \div \left(\frac{20}{4}\right) =$

2) $(-21) \times \frac{(-3)}{7} =$

3) $(-10) \times \left(-\frac{14}{5}\right) =$

4) $\left(\frac{3+(-13)}{2}\right) \div 5 =$

5) $18 \times \frac{24}{(-18)} =$

6) $(-90) \div \frac{(-45)}{14} =$

7) $\frac{\left(\frac{48}{4}\right)}{\left(\frac{60}{30}\right)} \times \frac{25}{(-5)} =$

8) $\left(2 \times \frac{24}{(-4)}\right) \div (-6) =$

9) $78 \div (-6) =$

10) $\frac{(-27)}{3} \times \left(-\frac{14}{7}\right) =$

11) $5 \times \left((-4) + \frac{15}{5}\right) =$

12) $\frac{(-48)}{4} \div (-2) =$

13) $\frac{(-36)}{12} \times (-2) =$

14) $(-10) \times (9) =$

15) $\frac{30}{(-6)} \times \frac{(-45)}{(-15)} =$

16) $(-100) \div \left(\frac{(-100)}{45}\right) =$

17) $(-80) \div (-20) =$

18) $(-6) \times (-11) =$

19) $(-3) \times \frac{(14 \times (-3))}{42} =$

20) $2 \times \left(-\frac{56}{8}\right) =$

21) $\frac{5}{2} \div \frac{10}{6} =$

22) $(-24) \div \frac{24}{10} + 5 =$

23) $\frac{25}{(-5)} \div \frac{1}{5} =$

24) $\frac{72 \div 12}{35 \div 5} \times 7 =$

25) $\frac{3(50 \div 5)}{30} \div \frac{10}{45} =$

26) $\frac{25}{5} \div \frac{25}{125} =$

27) $\frac{56}{7} \times \left(3 - \frac{42}{7}\right) =$

28) $3 \times \frac{24}{6} + 5 =$

29) $\frac{3}{10} \times \frac{-10}{7} =$

30) $\frac{(-25)}{11} \div \frac{40}{11} =$

31) $45 \div \left(\frac{4}{3} \div \frac{8}{6}\right) =$

32) $(-3) \div \left(\frac{(-20)}{66}\right) =$

33) $\left(\frac{45}{20}\right) \times \left(\frac{15}{20} \div \frac{10}{12}\right) =$

34) $\frac{1}{2} \times \left(3 - \frac{1}{3}\right) =$

Integers and Absolute Value

✍ *Write absolute value of each number.*

1) -78

2) -1

3) -65

4) 56

5) -98

6) -11

7) -21

8) 3

9) 2

10) -42

11) -61

12) -10

13) 36

14) -13

15) -33

16) -22

17) -19

18) 17

19) -14

20) -41

21) -98

✍ *Evaluate.*

22) $|-22| - |12| =$

23) $12 + |-15 - 10| - |-3| =$

24) $|-16| - 40 + 30 =$

25) $|-113| - |(-35) + 30| =$

26) $|12 - 4| + 6 - |-9| =$

27) $|-52| + |-10| =$

28) $|-2 + 8| + |7 - 7| =$

29) $|-12| + |-11| =$

✍ *Solve.*

30) You have money in your wallet, but you don't know the exact amount. When a friend asks you, you say that you have 50 dollars give or take 15. Use an absolute value equation to find least and biggest amount of money in your pocket?

31) The ideal selling price of a Toyota is 25000. The dealer allows this price to vary 5%. What is the lowest price this dealer can sell this Toyota?

Answers of Worksheets

Adding and Subtracting Integers

1) -45
2) -9
3) -60
4) -18
5) -19
6) -100

7) -72
8) -97
9) -51
10) 0
11) -10
12) 66

13) -30
14) -17
15) -15
16) -5
17) 1
18) 3

19) -28
20) 10
21) 6
22) 700

Multiplying and Dividing Integers

1) 55
2) -68
3) -20
4) -70
5) 44
6) -90

7) -196
8) 130
9) -280
10) -70
11) -15
12) 16

13) -12
14) 7
15) -6
16) 22
17) 9
18) 33

19) -25
20) -42
21) -6

Ordering Integers and Numbers

1) $-12, -10, 0, 2, 17, 36$
2) $-30, -12, -1, 2, 10, 21, 43$
3) $-14, -10, -3, 0, 14, 45$
4) $-100, 0, 10, 100$
5) $-50, -3, -2, 56$
6) $-10, -6, -1, 15, 18$
7) $-30, -20, -2, 0, 12, 15$

8) $-52, -12, -3, 12, 50$
9) $-9, -6, -1, 0, 2, 3$
10) $-14, -9, 10, 12, 21$
11) $10, 7, 0, -99$
12) $10.5, 0, -2, -4$
13) $33, -30, -33, -100$
14) $71, 51, 23, 12, 10, -3, -81$

15) $12, 6, 5, -2, -3, -32$
16) $13, 1, 0, -1, -13$
17) $79, 12, 0, -100$
18) $99, 23, 0, -1, -3$
19) $44, 19, -6, -100$

Arrange and Order, Comparing Integers

1) $34, 15, -3, -4$
2) $17, 0, -10, -14$
3) $15, -1, -15, -78$
4) $35, 12, -17, -45$

5) $71, -10, -14, -15, -30$
6) $62, 15, 14, 12, 0, -20$
7) $12, 1, 0, -1, -95, -369$
8) $62, 14, 7, 3, -1, -7, -41$

9) $100, 36, 5, -5, -100$
10) $99, 56, -45, -87, -110$
11) $<$
12) $<$

13) <
14) >
15) >
16) >
17) =
18) >

19) <
20) >
21) >
22) >
23) >
24) >

25) >
26) >
27) >
28) >

Order of Operations

1) 18
2) −1
3) −10
4) 3
5) −82
6) −40
7) −64

8) 20
9) 36
10) 0
11) 30
12) −52
13) −2
14) −11

15) 30
16) 20
17) 65
18) 9
19) 7.5
20) 8
21) −10

22) 33
23) −84
24) −14
25) 0
26) −108
27) $4.5

Mixed Integer Computations

1) −14
2) 9
3) 28
4) −1
5) −24
6) 28
7) 30
8) 2
9) −13

10) 18
11) −5
12) 6
13) 6
14) −90
15) −15
16) 45
17) 4
18) 66

19) 3
20) −14
21) $\frac{3}{2}$
22) −5
23) −25
24) 6
25) 4.5
26) 25
27) −24

28) 17
29) $-\frac{3}{7}$
30) $\frac{(-25)}{40}$
31) 45
32) $\frac{99}{10}$
33) $\frac{81}{40}$
34) $\frac{8}{6}$

Integers and Absolute Value

1) 78
2) 1

3) 65
4) 56

5) 98
6) 11

7) 21
8) 3

9) 2

10) 42

11) 61

12) 10

13) 36

14) 13

15) 33

16) 22

17) 19

18) 17

19) 14

20) 41

21) 98

22) 10

23) 34

24) 6

25) 108

26) 5

27) 62

28) 6

29) 23

30) 35,65

31) 23750

Chapter 3:

Proportions and Ratios

Math Topics that you'll learn in this part:

✓ Writing Ratios

✓ Simplifying Ratios

✓ Proportional Ratios

✓ Create a Proportion

✓ Similar Figures

✓ Similar Figure Word Problems

✓ Ratio and Rates Word Problems

Writing Ratios

🖎 *Express each ratio as a rate and unite rate.*

1) 150 miles on 5 gallons of gas.

2) 20 dollars for 4 books.

3) 100 miles on 8 gallons of gas

4) 30 inches of snow in 10 hours

🖎 *Express each ratio as a fraction in the simplest form.*

5) 6 feet out of 24 feet

6) 12 cakes out of 24 cakes

7) 7 dimes of 35 dimes

8) 16 dimes out of 48 coins

9) 21 cups to 56 cups

10) 36 gallons to 85 gallons

11) 18 miles out of 42 miles

12) 23 blue cars out of 46 cars

🖎 *Solve.*

13) In a telephone poll, 10 people said they like shopping and 20 people said they do not like shopping. What is the ratio of the number of people who do not like shopping to the number of people who like shopping?

14) There are 30 pink beads and 6 purple beads on Maria's necklace. What is the ratio of the number of pink beads to the number of purple beads?

15) 40 of the tables at Gary's Italian Restaurant are full and the other 8 tables are empty. What is the ratio of the number of full tables to the number of empty tables?

Simplifying Ratios

✎*Reduce each ratio.*

1) 42 : 70

2) 18 : 54

3) 15 : 45

4) 21 : 45

5) 10 : 60

6) 46 : 92

7) 50 : 20

8) 12 : 40

9) 90 : 45

10) 20 : 85

11) 28 : 40

12) 12 : 72

13) 24 : 12

14) 55 : 25

15) 39 : 13

16) 14 : 77

17) 18 : 66

18) 8 : 32

19) 45 : 100

20) 6 : 30

21) 17 : 85

22) 36 : 90

23) 15 : 80

24) 40 : 100

✎ *Each pair of figures is similar. Find the missing side.*

25)
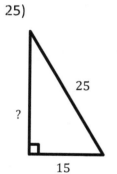
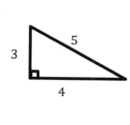

26)
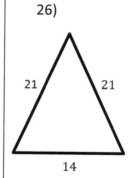
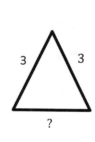

27)
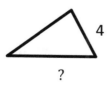
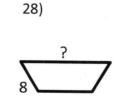

28)
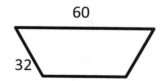

Create a Proportion

✎Create proportion from the given set of numbers.

1) $1, 15, 5, 3$

2) $12, 36, 4, 12$

3) $32, 8, 8, 2$

4) $17, 5, 51, 15$

5) $9, 7, 54, 42$

6) $56, 5, 8, 35$

7) $3, 5, 55, 33$

8) $12, 12, 3, 48$

✎Solve.

9) In a party, 10 soft drinks are required for every 12 guests. If there are 252 guests, how many soft drinks is required?

10) Mika can eat 21 hot dogs in 6 minutes. She wants to know how many minutes (m) it would take her to eat 35 hot dogs if she can keep up the same pace.

11) Mandy works construction. She knows that a 5-meter-long metal bar has a mass of 40kg. Mandy wants to figure out the mass (w) of a bar made of the same metal that is 3 meters long and the same thickness. What is the mass of the shorter bar?

12) Kwesi is putting on sunscreen. He uses 3ml to cover $45cm^2$ of his skin. He wants to know how many milliliters of sunscreen (g) he needs to cover $240cm^2$ of his skin. He assumes the relationship between milliliters of sunscreen and area is proportional. How many milliliters of sunscreen does Kwesi need to cover $240cm^2$ of his skin?

Similar Figures

✍ *Each pair of figures is similar. Find the missing side.*

1)

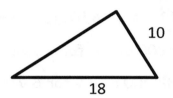

2)

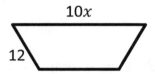

3)

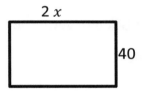

4)

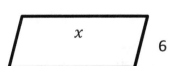

5)

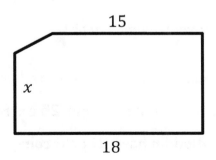

Simple Interest

✍ *Use simple interest to find the ending balance.*

1) $1,200 at 3% for 5 years.
2) $5,650 at 6% for 4 months.
3) $1600 at 8% for 8 years

4) $12,000 at 6.5% for 6 years.
5) $3200 at 4% for 7 years.
6) $32,500 at 8% for 6 years.

✍ *Solve.*

7) $300 interest is earned on a principal of $2000 at a simple interest rate of 5% interest per year. For how many years was the principal invested?

8) A new car, valued at $30,000, depreciates at 8% per year from original price. Find the value of the car 2 years after purchase.

9) Sara puts $4,000 into an investment yielding 7% annual simple interest; she left the money in for four years. How much interest does Sara get at the end of those four years?

10) You want to save $1,200 to buy your first self-driving magic carpet. You deposit $8,000 in a bank at an interest rate of 5% per annum. How many years do you have to wait before you can buy your magic carpet?

11) Aladdin has 12 extra gold coins in his magic bag. The Genie tells him that for every 100 gold coins he has in his magic bag, he will get 25 extra gold coins every year. How many years later will Aladdin have 21 gold coins in his bag?

Ratio and Rates Word Problems

✍ *Solve.*

1) In a party, 10 soft drinks are required for every 14 guests. If there are 266 guests, how many soft drinks is required?

2) In Jack's class, 12 of the students are tall and 8 are short. In Michael's class 26 students are tall and 14 students are short. Which class has a higher ratio of tall to short students?

3) Are these ratios equivalent? 13 cards to 78 animals 15marbles to 90 marbles.

4) The price of 4 apples at the Quick Market is$3. The price of 7 of the same apples at Walmart is $5.50. Which place is the better buy?

5) The bakers at a Bakery can make 200 bagels in 5 hours. How many bagels can they bake in 15 hours? What is that rate per hour?

6) You can buy 8 cans of green beans at a supermarket for $5.20. How much does it cost to buy 45 cans of green beans?

7) Finley makes 11 batch of her favorite shade of orange paint by mixing 55 liters of yellow paint with 33 liters of red paint. How many batches of orange paint can Finley make if she has 15 liters of red paint?

8) Quinn is playing video games at a virtual reality game room. The game room charges 20 dollars for every 30 minutes of play time. How much does Quinn need to pay for 150 minutes of play time.

Answers of Worksheets

Writing Ratios

1) $\frac{150\ miles}{5\ gallons}$, 30 miles per gallon

2) $\frac{20\ dollars}{4\ books}$, 5.00 dollars per book

3) $\frac{100\ miles}{8\ gallons}$, 12.5 miles per gallon

4) $\frac{30"\ of\ snow}{10\ hours}$, 3 inches of snow per hour

5) $\frac{1}{4}$ 7) $\frac{1}{5}$ 9) $\frac{3}{8}$ 11) $\frac{3}{7}$ 14) 5

6) $\frac{1}{2}$ 8) $\frac{1}{3}$ 10) $\frac{36}{85}$ 12) $\frac{1}{2}$ 15) 5

13) 2

Simplifying Ratios

1) 3:5	7) 5:2	13) 2:1	19) 9:20	25) 20
2) 1:3	8) 3:10	14) 11:5	20) 1:5	26) 2
3) 1:3	9) 2:1	15) 3:1	21) 1:6	27) 6
4) 7:15	10) 4:17	16) 2:11	22) 2:5	28) 15
5) 1:6	11) 7:10	17) 3:11	23) 3:16	
6) 1:2	12) 1:6	18) 1:4	24) 2:5	

Create a Proportion

1) $1:3 = 5:15$ 5) $7:42 = 9:54$ 9) 210

2) $12:36 = 4:12$ 6) $5:35 = 8:56$ 10) 10

3) $2:8 = 8:32$ 7) $3:33 = 5:55$ 11) 24

4) $5:15 = 17:51$ 8) $3:12 = 12:48$ 12) 16

Similar Figures

1) 9   2) 3   3) 24   4) 15   5) 6

Simple Interest

1) $1380.00   4) $16,680.00   7) 3 years   9) $1,120

2) $7,006.00   5) $4,096.00   8) $25,200   10) 3 years

3) $2,624.00   6) $48,100.00

11) %5

Ratio and Rates Word Problems

1) 190

2) The ratio for Michael's class is higher and equal to 13 to 7.

3) Yes! Both ratios are 1 to 6

4) The price at the Quick Market is a better buy.

5) 600, the rate is 40 per hour.

6) $29.25

7) 5

8) 100

Chapter 4:

Percent

Math Topics that you'll learn in this part:

✓ Percentage Calculations

✓ Converting Between Percent, Fractions, and Decimals

✓ Percent Problems

✓ Find What Percentage a Number Is of Another

✓ Find a Percentage of a Given Number

✓ Percent of Increase and Decrease

✓ Markup, Discount, and Tax

Percentage Calculations

✍ Calculate the percentages.

1) 10% of 50 =

2) 15% of 80 =

3) 50% of 26 =

4) 30% of 20 =

5) 45% of 100 =

6) 25% of 100 =

7) 70% of 30 =

8) 38% of 50 =

9) 20% of 50 =

10) 75% of 100 =

11) 65% of 80 =

12) 30% of 50 =

13) 20% of 0 =

14) 84% of 200 =

15) 12% of 100 =

16) 40% of 300 =

17) 30% of 60 =

18) 50% of 90 =

19) 30% of 45 =

20) 60% of 150 =

✍ Solve.

21) A test has 20 questions. If peter gets 80% correct, how many questions did peter missed?

22) In a school, 25 % of the teachers teach basic math. If there are 50 basic math teachers, how many teachers are there in the school?

23) 24 students in a class took an algebra test. If 18 students passed the test, what percent do not pass?

24) Yesterday, there were 20 problems assigned for math homework. Lucy got 18 out of 20 problems correct. What percentage did Lucy get correct?

25) Megan's Tea Shop has caffeinated tea and decaffeinated tea. The tea shop served 10 teas in all, 7 of which were caffeinated. What percentage of the teas were caffeinated?

Converting Between Percent, Fractions, and Decimals

✍ *Converting fractions to decimals.*

1) $\frac{35}{100}$ 4) $\frac{46}{100}$ 7) $\frac{91}{100}$

2) $\frac{32}{100}$ 5) $\frac{72}{100}$ 8) $\frac{36}{100}$

3) $\frac{56}{100}$ 6) $\frac{21}{100}$ 9) $\frac{98}{100}$

✍ *Write each decimal as a percent.*

10) 0.72   13) 0.42   16) 1.3

11) 0.962   14) 0.83   17) 0.035

12) 0.54   15) 0.452   18) 3.12

✍ *How many percentages have the sizes changed?*

19)

20)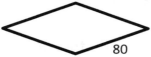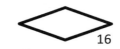

21)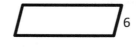

22)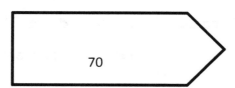

Percent Problems

✍ *Solve each problem.*

1) 60 is 120% of what?

2) 40% of what number is 50?

3) 27% of 142 is what number?

4) What percent of 125 is 30?

5) 30 is what percent of 120?

6) 44 is 25% of what?

7) 33 is 30% of what?

8) 52% of 150 is what?

9) 15 is what percent of 300?

10) What is 35% of 52 m?

11) What is 45% of 120 inches?

12) 18 inches is 40% of what?

✍ *Solve.*

13) Liam scored 21 out of 33 marks in Algebra, 37 out of 46 marks in science and 75 out of 95 marks in mathematics. In which subject his percentage of marks in best?

14) Ella require 50% to pass. If she gets 160 marks and falls short by 40 marks, what were the maximum marks she could have got?

15) There are 60 employees in a company. On a certain day, 36 were present. What percent showed up for work?

16) A metal bar weighs 24 ounces. 15% of the bar is gold. How many ounces of gold are in the bar?

17) A crew is made up of 12 women; the rest are men. If 20% of the crew are women, how many people are in the crew?

Find What Percentage a Number Is of Another

✍ Find the percentage of the numbers.

1) 10 is what percent of 40?

2) 12 is what percent of 240?

3) 151.2 is what percent of 270?

4) 14 is what percent of 112?

5) 6 is what percent of 30?

6) 17 is what percent of 85?

7) 39.6 is what percent of 88?

8) 420 is what percent of 350?

9) 13 is what percent of 104?

10) 9 is what percent of 225?

11) 75 is what percent of 50?

12) 11 is what percent of 55?

13) 300 is what percent of 1250?

14) 7.5 is what percent of 60?

15) 352 is what percent of 220?

16) 504 is what percent of 252?

17) 52 is what percent of 260?

18) 45 is what percent of 360?

✍ Solve

19) Challenger Elementary School has 800 students. Every Wednesday, 12% of the students stay after school for Chess Club. How many students attend Chess Club on Wednesdays?

20) Anastasia is grocery shopping with her father and wonders how much shopping is left to do. "We already have 60% of the items on our list," her father says. Anastasia sees 12 items in the cart. How many grocery items are on the list?

21) A gumball machine contains 23 green gumballs, 52 red gumballs, 34 blue gumballs, 61 yellow gumballs, and 30 pink gumballs. What percentage of the gumballs are red?

Find a Percentage of a Given Number

✎ *Find a Percentage of a Given Number.*

1) 25% of $50 =$ 8) 15% of $40 =$ 15) 45% of $90 =$

2) 40% of $90 =$ 9) 5% of $80 =$ 16) 40% of $120 =$

3) 11% of $69 =$ 10) 20% of $80 =$ 17) 30% of $9 =$

4) 12% of $60 =$ 11) 80% of $80 =$ 18) 65% of $200 =$

5) 45% of $66 =$ 12) 25% of $36 =$ 19) 66% of $10 =$

6) 38% of $55 =$ 13) 70% of $40 =$ 20) 36% of $50 =$

7) 65% of $30 =$ 14) 45% of $60 =$ 21) 96% of $80 =$

✎ *Solve.*

22) Luke and Matthew ran a lemonade stand on Saturday. They agreed that Matthew would get 60% of the profit because the lemonade stand was his idea. They made a profit of $25. How much money did Matthew make?

23) Mrs. Conley asks her class what kind of party they want to have to celebrate their excellent behavior. Out of all the students in the class, 5 want an ice cream party, 7 want a movie party, 10 want a costume party, and the rest are undecided. If 20% want an ice cream party, how many students are in the class?

24) There are 25 students in Ms. Nguyen's second-grade class. In the class election, 4 students voted for Benjamin, 12 voted for Sahil, and 9 voted for Maria. What percentage of the class voted for Maria?

Percent of Increase and Decrease

✍ *Find each percent change to the nearest percent. Increase or decrease.*

1) From 25 grams to 110 grams.

2) From 200 m to 50 m

3) From $520 to $102

4) From 256 ft. to 70 ft.

5) From 526 ft. to 800 ft.

6) From 25 inches to 125 inches

7) From 33 ft. to 163 ft.

8) From 536 miles to 76 miles

✍ *Solve.*

9) The population of a place in a particular year increased by 10%. Next year it decreased by 15%. Find the net increase or decrease percent in the initial population.

10) While measuring a line segment of length 5cm, it was measured 5.2cm by mistake. Find the percentage error in measuring the line segment.

11) A number is increased by 40% and then decreased by 40%. Find the net increase or decrease per cent.

12) The price of wheat increased by 10%. By how much per cent should mother reduce her consumption in the house so that her expenditure on wheat does not increase?

13) The football team at Riverside College plays in an old stadium that seats 31,780 people. This stadium will be demolished and a new one built that can hold 35% more fans. What will be the seating capacity of the new, bigger stadium?

Markup, Discount, and Tax

✍️ Find the selling price of each item.

1) Cost of a pen: $4.5, markup:.25%, discount: 20%, tax:5%

2) Cost of a puppy: $210, markup:20%, discount:15%

3) Cost of a shirt: $18.00, markup:22%, discount:20%

4) Cost of an oil change: $28.5, markup:55%

5) Cost of computer: $1,690.00, markup:15%

✍️ Solve.

6) Vanessa earns a base salary of $400.00 with an additional %5, percent commission on everything she sells. Vanessa sold $1650.00-dollar worth of items last week. What was Vanessa's total pay last week?

7) The pie store is having a %20 percent off sale on all its pies. If the pie you want regularly costs $18, how much would you save with the discount?

8) Zoe paid $18.60 in sales tax for purchasing a table. The sales tax rate is 12%, What was the price of Zoe's table before sales tax?

9) Daniel works at a nearby electronics store. He makes a commission of 15% on everything he sells. If he sells a laptop for $293.00, how much money does Daniel make in commission?

Answers of Worksheets

Percentage Calculations

1)	5	6)	25	11) 52	16) 120	21) 4
2)	12	7)	21	12) 15	17) 18	22) 200
3)	13	8)	19	13) 0	18) 45	23) 25%
4)	6	9)	10	14) 168	19) 13.5	24) 90%
5)	45	10) 75	15) 12	20) 90	25) 70%

Converting Between Percent, Fractions, and Decimals

1)	0.35	6)	0.21	11) 96.2%	16) 130%	21) 25%
2)	0.32	7)	0.91	12) 54%	17) 3.5%	22) 20%
3)	0.56	8)	0.36	13) 42%	18) 312%	
4)	0.46	9)	0.98	14) 83%	19) 75%	
5)	0.72	10) 72%	15) 45.2 %	20) 20%	

Percent Problems

1)	50	6)	176	11) 54 inches	15) 60%
2)	125	7)	110	12) 45 inches	16) 3.6 ounces
3)	38.34	8)	78	13) science, 80%	17) 60
4)	24%	9)	5%	14) 400	
5)	25%	10) 18.2 m		

Find What Percentage a Number Is of Another

1)	25%	6)	20%	11) 150%	16) 200%	21) 26%
2)	5%	7)	45%	12) 20%	17) 20%	
3)	56%	8)	120%	13) 24%	18) 12.5%	
4)	12.5%	9)	12.5%	14) 12.5%	19) 96	
5)	20%	10) 4%	15) 160%	20) 20	

Find a Percentage of a Given Number

1) 12.5	6) 20.9	11) 64	16) 48	21) 76.8
2) 36	7) 19.5	12) 9	17) 2.7	22) 15
3) 7.59	8) 6	13) 28	18) 130	23) 25
4) 7.2	9) 4	14) 27	19) 6.6	24) 36
5) 29.7	10) 16	15) 40.5	20) 18	

Percent of Increase and Decrease

1) 440% increase	6) 500% increase	11) 16% decrease
2) 75% decrease	7) 493% increase	12) $9\frac{1}{10}\%$
3) 80.4% decrease	8) 86% decrease	13) 42,903
4) 73% decrease	9) 6.5% decrease	
5) 52% increase	10) 4%	

Markup, Discount, and Tax

1) $4.725	4) $44.175	7) 3.6
2) $214.2	5) $1943.5	8) 16.61
3) $17.568	6) $482.50	9) 43.95

Chapter 5:

Algebraic Expressions

Topics that you'll learn in this part:

- ✓ Expressions and Variables
- ✓ Simplifying Variable Expressions
- ✓ Simplifying Polynomial Expressions
- ✓ The Distributive Property
- ✓ Evaluating One Variable
- ✓ Evaluating Two Variables
- ✓ Combining like Terms

Expressions and Variables

🖋 *Simplify each expression.*

1) $3x + 2x,$

   $Use\ x = 4$

2) $3(-3x + 9) + 3x,$

   $Use\ x = 2$

3) $(2x + 5) + (-2x),$

   $Use\ x = 4$

4) $(6x - 3)(2x + 1),$

   $Use\ x = 2$

5) $(2x + 5) + (3y - 3),$

   $Use\ x = 2, y = -2$

6) $(5x - 1)(2x + y),$

   $Use\ x = -1, y = 3$

7) $(2y)(2y - 3x),$

   $Use\ x = 2, y = 1$

8) $(5x + 2y)y,$

   $Use\ x = 4, y = 2$

9) $3x + 2(2y - 2),$

   $Use\ x = 4, y = 2$

10) $x + x(y - x),$

   $Use\ x = 1, y = 2$

11) $2 + y(y - 2x),$

   $Use\ x = 3, y = 1$

12) $x(2y - 3x),$

   $Use\ x = -2, y = 2$

🖋 *Simplify each expression.*

13) $2 + 2x - 3x =$

14) $4z + 2(z + 6) =$

15) $4y + 5 + 3y =$

16) $4w - 5 - 3w =$

17) $3m - 4(2m + 1) =$

18) $2t - 4(2 - t) =$

19) $-2k + 5 + 9k =$

20) $3(2d + 2) + (-6d) =$

21) $(-5)(5q + 3) - 3q =$

22) $(-a) + (-3)(1 - a) =$

23) $(2x - 1) - (6 - x) =$

24) $(-5)(2m + 2) + 3m =$

25) $9x - 4 - 5x + 3 =$

26) $(-3z) + (-2)(1 - z) =$

27) $14n - 3m + 12m - 19n =$

28) $33x - 5(6x - 1) =$

Simplifying Variable Expressions

✎ **Simplify each expression.**

1) $-6-2x^2+4x^2=$

2) $3+10x^2+2+5x^2=$

3) $4x^2+4(2x+1)=$

4) $4x^2-x(4x+1)=$

5) $4(x^2-1)+4x(2x+1)=$

6) $(x^3+4)+x(2x^2+1)=$

7) $4x^2-19+4(2x^2+1)=$

8) $x^4+4(2x+1)-2x^4=$

9) $(3x^2+1)x+(x^3-x)=$

10) $(2x-1)(2x+1)=$

11) $(5x-2)(5x+2)=$

12) $(x+4)(x+4)=$

13) $2x^2+5x-10x^2-2x=$

14) $32x-15(2x+2)=$

15) $(2x+1)x+(-3x^2)-x=$

16) $2(2-x)+2(2x-4)=$

17) $3(x+9)=$

18) $(-6)(8x-4)=$

19) $7x+3-3x=$

20) $-2-x^2-6x^2=$

21) $3+10x^2+2=$

22) $8x^2+6x+7x^2=$

23) $x^2-2x+4x^2-1=$

24) $x^3(2x-x^2-1)-x^5=$

25) $Z^2-Z(2Z+5)=$

26) $4x^2+2x(3-5x)=$

27) $10m\left(\frac{m-15}{5}\right)+4m=$

28) $3x^2-2x(4x+1)=$

✎ **Simplify.**

29) $x(3x+3), x=2$

30) $4-5x+9x-3, x=1$

31) $(2x+3)(2x+1), x=2$

32) $x(3x-14), x=4$

33) $2x+9-3x+2, x=-2$

34) $x(x+4)+2x, x=2$

35) $(15x-25)x, x=3$

36) $x+x(6x-1), x=-1$

37) $x+(7-x), x=3$

38) $(3x-1)(x+2), x=-2$

Simplifying Polynomial Expressions

✍ *Simplify each polynomial.*

1) $(2x^3 + 5x^2) - (12x + 2x^2) =$

2) $(2x^5 + 2x^3) - (7x^3 + 6x^2) =$

3) $(12x^4 + 4x^2) - (2x^2 - 6x^4) =$

4) $14x - 3x^2 - 2(6x^2 + 6x^3) =$

5) $(5x^3 - 3) + 5(2x^2 - 3x^3) =$

6) $(4x^3 - 2x) - 2(4x^3 - 2x^4) =$

7) $2(4x - 3x^3) - 3(3x^3 + 4x^2) =$

8) $(2x^2 - 2x) - (2x^3 + 5x^2) =$

9) $2x^3 - (4x^4 + 2x) + x^2 =$

10) $x^4 - 2(x^2 + x) + 3x =$

11) $(2x^2 - x^4) - (4x^4 - x^2) =$

12) $4x^2 - 5x^3 + 15x^4 - 12x^3 =$

13) $2x^2 - 5x^4 + 14x^4 - 11x^3 =$

14) $2x^2 + 5x^3 - 7x^2 + 12x =$

15) $2x^4 - 5x^5 + 8x^{\,4} - 8x^2 =$

16) $5x^3 + 15x - x^2 - 2x^3 =$

17) $14x^3 + 5 - 3(3x^2 + 1) =$

18) $2(3x + 1) + 2x(x - 2) =$

19) $-10x^2 + 4x^5 + 12x(1 + x) =$

20) $-3x - x^3 + x(3x + 3) =$

✍ *Solve.*

21) If $G = t^2 - 5t + 6$ and $H = -8t^2 + 7t - 9$ then what is the sum of sum G and H?

22) Subtract $6x^2 - 7x - 11$ from $5x^2 - 4x + 3$.

23) A polynomial of the 4th degree with a leading coefficient of 7 and a constant term of 8. Which answer is correct?

A: $7x^5 + 6x - 8$

B: $7x^4 + 6x + 8$

C: $7x^2 - 6x + 8$

D: $7x^4 + 8x + 7$

The Distributive Property

✍ *Use the distributive property to simply each expression.*

1) $x(3 - 2x) =$

2) $(-2)(2x - 1) + x =$

3) $3x(2 - x) =$

4) $(x + 1)(x - 1) =$

5) $(-5)(x + 3 - 3x) =$

6) $14(2x + 5) =$

7) $(x + 2)2x =$

8) $12(3x - 1) =$

9) $3x(x - 4) =$

10) $7x(1 + x) + 14 =$

11) $(-2x)x - 4x(4 + 5x) + 2 =$

12) $2x(4 - x) + (3x^2 + 4) =$

13) $(x + 1)(x - 1) + (-2x)x =$

14) $2x(x^2 + x + 1) + x(x - 1) =$

15) $3x(x - 1) - 3x(1 - x) =$

16) $(-2)(x - 1) + 10(x + 2) =$

17) $(3x + 1)(x - 1) + 2x^2 =$

18) $5(x + 1) + (-2x)(x + 2) =$

19) $x^2(x - 1) + x(2x^2 + 3) =$

20) $2(2 + 3x) =$

21) $3(5 + 5x) =$

22) $4(3x - 8) =$

23) $(6x - 2)(-2) =$

24) $(-3)(x + 2) =$

25) $(2 + 2x)5 =$

26) $(-4)(4 - 2x) =$

27) $-(-2 - 5x) =$

28) $(-6x + 2)(-1) =$

29) $(-5)(x - 2) =$

30) $-(7 - 3x) =$

31) $8(8 + 2x) =$

32) $2(12 + 2x) =$

33) $(-6x + 8)4 =$

34) $(3 - 6x)(-7) =$

35) $(-12)(2x + 1) =$

36) $(8 - 2x)9 =$

37) $5(7 + 9x) =$

38) $11(5x + 2) =$

39) $(-4x + 6)6 =$

40) $(3 - 6x)(-8) =$

41) $(-12)(2x - 3) =$

42) $(10 - 2x)9 =$

Evaluating One Variable

✍ *Simplify each algebraic expression.*

1) $4 - (2x + 1), x = 3$

2) $3x + 5, x = 2$

3) $-2x - 7, x = -2$

4) $3x - 5, x = -3$

5) $3x + 6, x = 3$

6) $12x - 10, x = 2$

7) $1 - 2x + 4, x = -3$

8) $5 - 3x, x = -3$

9) $\frac{15}{x+4} - 3, x = -7$

10) $\frac{x+2}{4} + 2x, x = 6$

11) $\frac{3x(x-2)}{(x+6)}, x = 3$

12) $\frac{4x+2}{x} + 4x, x = 2$

13) $\frac{8}{x+1} - 12x, x = 3$

14) $2x + \frac{x}{8}, x = 8$

15) $(2x + 1) + 3x, x = -2$

16) $2x + \frac{x+3}{2}, x = 3$

17) $(5x - 1) + (3x + 2), x = 3$

18) $(-x)(5x - 4) + 2x, x = 3$

19) $4x + 5 + 2x - 2, x = 2$

20) $(-2x)(x - 1), x = -2$

21) $-3x + 5(3 - x), x = 4$

22) $\frac{3x+5}{1-x} + 2x, x = 3$

23) $\frac{2(2x-1)}{(1-x)+2x+1}, x = -4$

24) $\frac{2x+5}{x} + 4x, x = 5$

25) $3x - \frac{1-x}{1+x}, x = -5$

26) $4x + 2 - 6x, x = 1$

27) $\frac{2x+5+14x}{x(1-x)}, x = 2$

28) $\frac{3x(1-2x)}{x+2}, x = 3$

29) $3x^2 + 2x - 1, x = -2$

30) $\frac{32x-20}{x+4}, x = -3$

31) $\frac{12x-10}{2x}, x = 1$

32) $(3x - 4) - 5x, x = -3$

33) $\frac{-2x+1-x}{x-3}, x = -3$

34) $4x(x + 1) + x, x = -4$

35) $2t(5 - t), t = -5$

36) $-2y(3y + 4), y = -2$

37) $4m + \frac{3m-1}{m+1}, m = 3$

38) $(3y + 1) + (2y - 3), y = 0$

39) $5G(3 + 2G) - G, G = -1$

Evaluating Two Variables

✍️*Simplify each algebraic expression.*

1) $2(x + 1) + y - 3 + 2$,

   $x = 3, y = 1$

2) $\left(-\frac{y+3}{x}\right) + 3y$

   $x = 5, y = 7$

3) $(-2a)(-2a - 2b)$,

   $a = -2, b = 3$

4) $2(x - 2y)$,

   $x = -2, y = 3$

5) $3x + 2 - 2y$,

   $x = 5, y = -2$

6) $2 + 2(-2x - 3y)$,

   $x = 4, y = 1$

7) $12(x + y + 1) + y$,

   $x = -1, y = 3$

8) $(2x + 1)y$

   $x = 3, y = 2$

9) $(x + 12) \div 2y$

   $x = 2, y = -1$

10) $(2x + y)2y + 2$,

    $x = 2, y = 5$

11) $2(x + y) + 5y$,

    $x = 2, y = 3$

12) $4y(2x + y)$,

    $x = -2, y = 2$

13) $2x + 5 - 3y$,

    $x = 2, y = -3$

14) $\frac{3x+5}{2y-2} + 2xy$,

    $x = -2, y = -1$

15) $3x + 2xy - 3y + 2$,

    $x = 4, y = 2$

16) $3y - \frac{42x}{2y} + 2y$,

    $x = 1, y = -3$

17) $2(2y - x) - 3(xy - 1)$,

    $x = 2, y = -3$

18) $\frac{y}{-x} + 2xy + 3y$,

    $x = -3, y = -6$

19) $2x - 3y + 2(x - y)$,

    $x = 4, y = -4$

20) $\frac{2x-y}{2x+y} - 2xy$,

    $x = -3, y = 2$

21) $4xy - 3x + y$,

    $x = 2, y = -1$

Combining like Terms

✎ *Simplify each expression.*

1) $3x + 2 - 5x + 1 =$

2) $2x(1 + x) + 2 =$

3) $2(x - 1) + 3x - 1 =$

4) $2(2 - x) + 2x + 2 =$

5) $5x + 2 + 7x + 3x =$

6) $x + 2(3x - 2) =$

7) $(x + 1)(x - 1) - 2x =$

8) $9x - 2 - 5x + 7 =$

9) $2(2x + 1) - 5x =$

10) $2 + 2x - 5x - 3 =$

11) $12x - 2(1 - x) =$

12) $(3 - x)(x - 1) =$

13) $x + 1 + 3x + 4x =$

14) $3x + 9x - 2x + 7 =$

15) $-12x + 3 - x(-3) =$

16) $3x + 5x - 4x + 10 =$

17) $5(x - 2) + x(12 - 4) =$

18) $32x - 4 - 17x - 2x =$

19) $22x + 14x + 2 - 18x =$

20) $(x + 3) + 3x + 5x - 2 =$

21) $2 - 8x + 3 + 5x =$

22) $33x - 12x + 2x =$

23) $2(3x - 2) + (-4x + 4) =$

24) $2x - 4x + 7x + 2 =$

25) $72x - 33x + (-20x) =$

26) $3 - 5x - 12x + 25x =$

27) $12x - 5 + 4x - 3 =$

28) $12x + 4x - 21 =$

29) $5 + 2x - 8 =$

30) $(-2x + 6)2 =$

31) $7 + 3x + 6x - 4 =$

32) $9(x - 7x) - 5 =$

33) $7(3x + 6) + 2x =$

34) $3x - 12 - 5x =$

35) $2(4 + 3x) - 7x =$

36) $22x + 6 + 2x =$

37) $(-5x) + 12 + 7x =$

38) $(-3x) - 9 + 15x =$

39) $2(5x + 7) + 8x =$

40) $2(9 - 3x) - 17x =$

41) $-4x - (6 - 14x) =$

42) $(-4) - (3)(5x + 8) =$

Answers of Worksheets

Expressions and Variables

1) 20
2) 15
3) 5
4) 45
5) 0
6) −6
7) −8
8) 48
9) 16
10) 2
11) −3
12) −20
13) $-x + 2$
14) $6z + 12$
15) $7y + 5$
16) $w - 5$
17) $-5m - 4$
18) $6t - 8$
19) $7k + 5$
20) 6
21) $-28q - 15$
22) $2a - 3$
23) $3x - 7$
24) $-7m - 10$
25) $4x - 1$
26) $-z - 2$
27) $-5n + 9m$
28) $3x + 5$

Simplifying Variable Expressions

1) $2x^2 - 6$
2) $15x^2 + 5$
3) $4x^2 + 8x + 4$
4) $-x$
5) $12x^2 + 4x - 4$
6) $3x^2 + x + 4$
7) $12x^2 + x - 19$
8) $-x^4 + 8x + 4$
9) $4x^3$
10) $4x^2 - 1$
11) $25x^2 - 4$
12) $x^2 + 8x + 16$
13) $-8x^2 + 3x$
14) $-2x - 30$
15) $-x^2$
16) $2x - 4$
17) $3x + 27$
18) $-48x + 24$
19) $4x + 3$
20) $-7x^2 - 2$
21) $10x^2 + 5$
22) $15x^2 + 6x$
23) $5x^2 - 2x - 1$
24) $-2x^5 + 2x^4 - x^3$
25) $-Z^2 - 5Z$
26) $-6x^2 + 6x$
27) $2m^2 - 26m$
28) $-5x^2 - 2x$
29) 18
30) 5
31) 35
32) −8
33) 13
34) 16
35) 60
36) 6
37) 7
38) 0

Simplifying Polynomial Expressions

1) $2x^3 + 3x^2 - 12x$
2) $2x^5 - 5x^3 - 6x^2$
3) $18x^4 + 2x^2$
4) $-12x^3 - 15x^2 + 14x$
5) $-10x^3 + 10x^2 - 3$
6) $4x^4 - 4x^3 - 2x$
7) $-15x^3 - 12x^2 + 8x$
8) $-2x^3 - 3x^2 - 2x$
9) $-4x^4 + 2x^3 + x^2 - 2x$
10) $x^4 - 2x^2 + x$
11) $-5x^4 + 3x^2$
12) $15x^4 - 17x^3 + 4x^2$
13) $9x^4 - 11x^3 + 2x^2$
14) $5x^3 - 5x^2 + 12x$
15) $-5x^5 + 10x^4 - 8x^2$

16) $3x^3 - x^2 + 15x$

17) $14x^3 - 9x^2 + 2$

18) $2x^2 + 2x + 2$

19) $4x^5 + 2x^2 + 12x$

20) $-x^3 + 3x^2$

21) $-7t^2 + 2t - 3$

22) $x^2 - 3x - 14$

23) B

The Distributive Property

1) $-2x^2 - 3x$

2) $-3x + 2$

3) $-3x^2 + 6x$

4) $x^2 - 1$

5) $10x - 15$

6) $28x + 70$

7) $2x^2 + 4x$

8) $36x - 12$

9) $3x^2 - 12x$

10) $7x^2 + 7x + 14$

11) $-22x^2 - 16x + 2$

12) $x^2 + 8x + 4$

13) $2x^2 - x - 1$

14) $2x^3 + 3x^2 + x$

15) $6x^2 - 6x$

16) $8x + 22$

17) $5x^2 - 2x - 1$

18) $-2x^2 + x + 5$

19) $3x^3 - x^2 + 3x$

20) $6x + 4$

21) $15x + 15$

22) $12x - 32$

23) $-12x + 4$

24) $-3x - 6$

25) $10x + 10$

26) $8x - 16$

27) $5x + 2$

28) $6x - 2$

29) $-5x + 10$

30) $3x - 7$

31) $16x + 64$

32) $4x + 24$

33) $-24x + 32$

34) $42x - 21$

35) $-24x - 12$

36) $-18x + 72$

37) $45x + 35$

38) $55x + 22$

39) $-24x + 36$

40) $48x - 24$

41) $-24x + 36$

42) $-18x + 90$

Evaluating one Variables

1) -3

2) 11

3) -3

4) -14

5) 15

6) 14

7) 11

8) 14

9) -8

10) 14

11) 1

12) 13

13) -34

14) 17

15) -9

16) 9

17) 25

18) -27

19) 15

20) -12

21) -17

22) -1

23) 9

24) 23

25) $-13\frac{2}{4}$

26) 0

27) $-\frac{37}{2}$

28) -9

29) 7

30) -116

31) 1

32) 2

33) $-\frac{5}{3}$

34) 44

35) -100

36) -8

37) 14

38) -2

39) -4

Evaluating Two Variables

1) 8	6) −20	11) 25	16) −8	21) −15
2) 19	7) 39	12) −16	17) 5	
3) −8	8) 14	13) 18	18) 16	
4) −16	9) −7	14) $4\frac{1}{4}$	19) 36	
5) 21	10) 92	15) 24	20) 14	

Combining like Terms

1) $3 - 2x$	16) $4x + 10$	31) $-54x - 5$
2) $2x^2 + 2x + 2$	17) $13x - 10$	32) $23x + 42$
3) $5x - 3$	18) $13x - 4$	33) $-2x - 12$
4) 6	19) $18x + 2$	34) $-x + 8$
5) $15x + 2$	20) $9x + 1$	35) $24x + 6$
6) $7x - 4$	21) $5 - 3x$	36) $2x + 12$
7) $x^2 - 4x + 1$	22) $23x$	37) $12x - 9$
8) $4x + 5$	23) $2x$	38) $18x + 14$
9) $2 - x$	24) $5x + 2$	39) $-23x + 18$
10) $-3x - 1$	25) $19x$	40) $10x - 6$
11) $14x - 2$	26) $8x + 3$	41) $-15x - 28$
12) $-x^2 + 4x - 3$	27) $16x - 8$	
13) $8x + 1$	28) $16x - 21$	
14) $10x + 7$	29) $2x - 3$	
15) $3 - 9x$	30) $-4x + 129x + 3$	

Chapter 6:

Equations and Inequalities

Topics that you'll learn in this part:

- ✓ One–Step Equations
- ✓ One–Step Equation Word Problems
- ✓ Two–Step Equations
- ✓ Two–Step Equation Word Problems
- ✓ Multi–Step Equations
- ✓ Graphing Single–Variable Inequalities
- ✓ One–Step Inequalities
- ✓ Multi-Step Inequalities

One–Step Equations

✎ *Solve each equation.*

1) $2x + 4 = 18$

2) $22 = (-8) + 3x$

3) $3x = (-30) + x$

4) $(-35) - x = (-6x)$

5) $(-6) = 4 + 10x$

6) $6 + 2x = (-2)$

7) $20x - 20 = (-220)$

8) $18 = 3x + 3$

9) $(-25) + 2x = (-17)$

10) $5x + 5 = (-45)$

11) $3x - 12 = (-21)$

12) $x - 2 = (-8)$

13) $(-30) = x - 18$

14) $8 = 2x - 2$

15) $(-6x) - 6 = 36$

16) $(-55) = (-5x) + 10$

17) $2x - 15 = 25$

18) $8x - 16 = 32$

19) $24 = (-6x)$

20) $8x + 4 = 68$

21) $50x + 50 = 300$

✎ *Write each sentence as an equation.*

22) Eight less than $\frac{1}{3}$ a number M is -13.

23) A number of multiplied by -12.3 is -73.

24) Twice a number, decreased by twenty-nine, is seven.

25) Thirty-two is twice a number increased by eight.

26) Twelve is sixteen less than four times a number.

27) The sum of eight and a number is five less than seventy.

28) Ten less than a number z is twenty-five.

29)   Seven less than a number is sixty.

30) The sum of ten and a number is two less than thirty.

31) Seventeen less than a number x is fifty-three.

32) The sum of L and 15 is eight less than eighty-two.

33) The sum of eight and a number is ten less than eighteen.

One–Step Equation Word Problems

✎ *Solve.*

1) Thira has read 110 pages of a 290-page book. She reads 20 pages each day. How many days will it take to finish?

2) You and a friend split the cost of a moped rental. Your friend pays the bill. You owe your friend only $12, because your friend owed you $9 from yesterday. How much was the total bill?

3) Mr. Herman's class is selling candy for a school fundraiser. The class has a goal of raising $500 by selling c boxes of candy. For every box they sell, they make$5.5. How many boxes of candy they need to sell?

4) Lindsey is helping her uncle plant an apple orchard. After picking up a truckload of trees, they plant 20 of them. The next day, they still have 50 trees left to plant. Find the total number of trees in the original truckload?

5) Tina is baking chocolate chip cookies for a party at school. She leaves 12 at home for her family and brings the remaining 24 cookies to school to share with her classmates. Find the total number of cookies that Tina bakes?

6) The Laughing Lollipop candy store is holding a raffle, and Preston wins the grand prize! He wins a gift card to the store, as well as a bag of giant lollipops. He gives 21 lollipops to his friends, and he keeps the remaining 3 lollipops. Find the total number of lollipops in the bag?

Two–Step Equations

✎ *Solve each equation.*

1) $2(4 + x) = 20$

2) $(-2)(x + 3) = 42$

3) $3(2x - 4) = (-36)$

4) $6(2 - 2x) = 12$

5) $10(4x + 4) = (-60)$

6) $5(2x + 5) = 45$

7) $2(7 - 2x) = (-34)$

8) $(-4)(2x - 4) = 48$

9) $4(x - 5) = 8$

10) $\frac{2x - 10}{2} = 12$

11) $\frac{3x + 3}{9} = 10$

12) $15 = (-5)(3x - 6)$

13) $\frac{12 - x}{5} = 6$

14) $12 = (-12) + \frac{4x}{8}$

15) $\frac{24 + 3x}{4} = 9$

16) $(-2)(5 - 4x) = 70$

17) $(-11x) + 15 = 26$

18) $\frac{-24 - 8x}{6} = 8$

19) $\frac{2x - 12}{7} = 6$

20) $\frac{(-8) + 3x}{10} = \frac{2}{5}$

21) $\frac{2x + 2}{2} = 5$

✎ *Fill in the blank with the appropriate number*

22) $6 = \frac{x}{\square} + 2, x = 16$

23) $\square + \frac{x}{4} = -5, x = 4$

24) $0 = 4 + \frac{n}{\square}, n = -20$

25) $-1 = \frac{\square + x}{6}, x = -11$

26) $\frac{m + \square}{3} = 8, m = 15$

27) $2(n + 5) = \square, n = -6$

28) $144 = \square(x + 5), x = -17$

29) $10 - 6x = \square, x = 19$

30) $\frac{x + 5}{\square} = -1, x = 11$

31) $-10 = \square + 5x, x = 0$

32) $-10 = 10(x - \square), x = 8$

33) $\frac{x}{9} + \square = -2, x = -9$

34) $7(9 + x) = \square, x = 3$

35) $8 + \frac{x}{\square} = 5, x = 12$

36) $-243 = \square(10 + x), x = 17$

37) $-15 = (\square)x + 10, x = 5$

38) $-4 = \frac{x}{\square} - 5, x = 20$

Two–Step Equation Word Problems

✎*Solve.*

1) Aliyah had $24 to spend on seven pencils. After buying them she had $10. How much did each pencil cost?

2) Maria bought seven boxes. A week later half of all her boxes were destroyed in a fire. There are now only 22 boxes left. With how many did she start?

3) Sara Wong spent half of his weekly allowance playing arcade games. To earn more money his parents let him weed the garden for $6.55. What is his weekly allowance if he ended with $11.01?

4) Rob had some paper with which to make note cards. On his way to his room he found two more pieces to use. In his room he cut each piece of paper in half. When he was done, he had 22 half-pieces of paper. With how many sheets of paper did he start?

5) The Cooking Club made some pies to sell during lunch to raise money for an end-of-year banquet. The cafeteria contributed two pies to the club. Each pie was then cut into seven pieces and sold. There was a total of 84 pieces to sell. How many pies did the club make?

6) Adam won 59 lollipops playing hoops at the county fair. At school he gave two to every student in his math class. He only has 3 remaining. How many students are in his class?

Multi–Step Equations

✏️ *Solve each equation.*

1) $2(2x - 1) = 10 + x$

2) $(-3)(2 - x) = 30 - 3x$

3) $2x + 14 = 3(10 + 2x)$

4) $3x - 24 = 2(10 - x) + x$

5) $10x + 4 = (-36) - x + x$

6) $12x + 1 = 8x - 59$

7) $15x - 12 - 12x = 7x$

8) $(-3x) + 2(x + 1) = 4(6 + x) + 3$

✏️ *Solve.*

9) Tickets to a fundraiser are $14 if purchased ahead of time and $25 if purchased at the door. The total amount raised from all ticket sales was $625. If eleven tickets were purchased at the door, how many tickets were purchased ahead of time?

10) On Friday, you raked leaves for 4 neighbors, on Saturday you raked leaves for 5 neighbors, and on Sunday you raked leaves for 3 neighbors. Over the three days you earned a total of $135. If you were paid the same amount at each house, write and solve an equation to determine how much you earned per house.

11) Your school is having a fundraiser. You are selling candy bars that have been donated by the Hershey Company. You set a personal goal of raising $200 for your school and met that goal. You sold a total of 120 candy bars and one neighbor gave you a $20 donation without taking any candy bars. Write and solve an equation to determine how much each candy bar sold for?

Graphing Single–Variable Inequalities

✏️ *Draw a graph for each inequality.*

1) $x > 2$

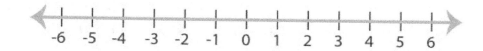

2) $x < 5$

3) $x > -1$

4) $x > 3$

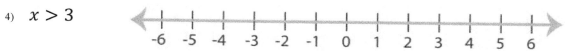

5) $x < -5$

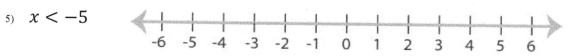

6) $x > -2$

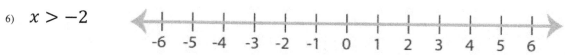

7) $x < 0$

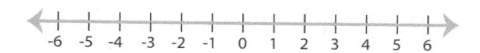

8) $x > 4$

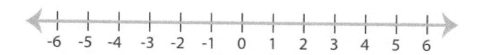

One–Step Inequalities

✐ *Solve each inequality and graph it.*

1) $x + 2 \geq 3$

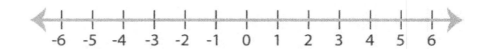

2) $x - 1 \leq 2$

3) $2x \geq 12$

4) $4 + x \leq 5$

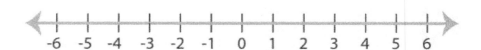

5) $x + 3 \leq -3$

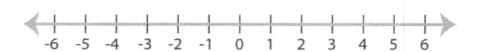

6) $4x \geq 16$

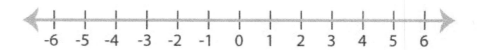

7) $9x \leq 18$

8) $x + 2 \geq 7$

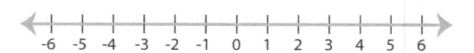

Multi-Step Inequalities

✎ *Solve each inequality.*

1) $x - 2 \leq 6$

2) $3 - x \leq 3$

3) $2x - 4 \leq 8$

4) $3x - 5 \geq 16$

5) $x - 5 \geq 10$

6) $2x - 8 \leq 6$

7) $8x - 2 \leq 14$

8) $-5 + 3x \leq 10$

9) $2(x - 3) \leq 6$

10) $7x - 5 \leq 9$

11) $4x - 21 < 19$

12) $2x - 3 < 21$

13) $17 - 3x \geq -13$

14) $9 + 4x < 21$

15) $3 + 2x \geq 19$

16) $6 + 2x < 32$

17) $4x - 1 < 7$

18) $3(3 - 2x) \geq -15$

19) $-(3 + 4x) < 13$

20) $20 - 8x \geq -28$

21) $-3(x - 7) > 21$

22) $\dfrac{2x + 6}{4} \leq 10$

23) $\dfrac{4x + 8}{2} \leq 12$

24) $\dfrac{3x - 8}{7} > 1$

25) $4 + \dfrac{x}{3} < 7$

26) $\dfrac{9x}{7} - 7 < 2$

27) $\dfrac{4x + 12}{4} > 1$

28) $15 + \dfrac{x}{5} < 12$

Answers of Worksheets

One–Step Equations

1) 7
2) 10
3) −15
4) 7
5) −1
6) −4
7) −10
8) 5
9) 4
10) −10
11) −3

12) −6
13) −12
14) 5
15) −5
16) 13
17) 20
18) 6
19) −4
20) 8
21) 5
22) $8 - \frac{1}{3}M = -13$

23) $(-12.3)f = -73$
24) $2x - 29 = 7$
25) $2x + 8 = 32$
26) $16 - 4x = 12$
27) $8 + x = 5 - 70$
28) $10 - z = 25$
29) $7 - x = 60$
30) $10 + x = 2 - 30$
31) $17 - x = 53$
32) $l + 15 = 8 - 82$
33) $8 + x = 10 - 8$

One–Step Equation Word Problems

1) 9   2) 42   3) 91   4) 30   5) 36   6) 24

Two–Step Equations

1) 6
2) −24
3) −4
4) 0
5) −2.5
6) 2
7) 12
8) −4

9) 7
10) 17
11) 29
12) 1
13) −18
14) 48
15) 4
16) 10

17) −1
18) −9
19) 27
20) 4
21) 4
22) 4
23) −6
24) 5

25) 5
26) 9
27) −2
28) −12
29) −104
30) −16
31) −10
32) −9

33) −1
34) 84
35) −4
36) −9
37) −1
38) 20

Two–Step Equation Word Problems

1) $2   2) 37   3) $8.92   4) 9   5) 10   6) 28

Multi–Step Equations

1) 4

2) 6

3) −4

4) 11

5) −4

6) −15

7) −3

8) −5

9) 25

10) 11.25

11) 1.5

Graphing Single–Variable Inequalities

1)

2)

3)

4)
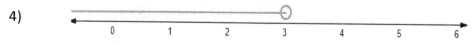

5)

6)

7)

8)
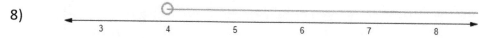

One–Step Inequalities

1)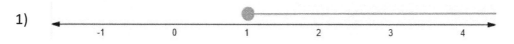

2)

3)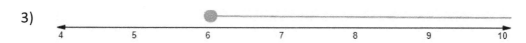

4)

5)

6)

7)

8)

Multi-Step Inequalities

1) $x \leq 8$

2) $x \geq 0$

3) $x \leq 6$

4) $x \geq 7$

5) $x \geq 15$

6) $x \leq 7$

7) $x \leq 2$

8) $x \leq 5$

9) $x \leq 6$

10) $x \leq 2$

11) $x < 10$

12) $x < 12$

13) $x \leq 10$

14) $x < 3$

15) $x \geq 8$

16) $x < 13$

17) $x < 2$

18) $x \leq 4$

19) $x > -4$

20) $x \leq 6$

21) $x < 0$

22) $x \leq 17$

23) $x \leq 4$

24) $x > 5$

25) $x < 9$

26) $x < 7$

27) $x > -2$

28) $x < -15$

Chapter 7:

Systems of Equations

Topics that you'll learn in this part:

- ✓ Solving Systems of Equations by Substitution
- ✓ Solving Systems of Equations by Elimination
- ✓ Systems of Equations Word Problems

Solving Systems of Equations by Substitution

✍ *Solve each system of equation by substitution.*

1) $\begin{cases} x + 4 = y \\ 2x + y = 1 \end{cases}$

2) $\begin{cases} 2x + y = 2 \\ x - y = 10 \end{cases}$

3) $\begin{cases} 4y - 2 = x \\ x + 2y = 4 \end{cases}$

4) $\begin{cases} 1 - x = 2y \\ 2x - 2y = -16 \end{cases}$

5) $\begin{cases} 3x - y = 6 \\ 2x + y = 14 \end{cases}$

6) $\begin{cases} 2x + 1 = 1 - y \\ x - 3y = 28 \end{cases}$

7) $\begin{cases} y - 3x = 4 \\ 2(x + y) + 5 = -11 \end{cases}$

8) $\begin{cases} 9 - 6x = 3y \\ 3x + y = 1 \end{cases}$

9) $\begin{cases} y = 7x - 10 \\ y = -3 \end{cases}$

10) $\begin{cases} y = -8x \\ 2x + 4y = 0 \end{cases}$

11) $\begin{cases} 6x - 11 = y \\ -2x - 3y = -7 \end{cases}$

12) $\begin{cases} 2x - 3y = -1 \\ x - 1 = y \end{cases}$

13) $\begin{cases} -3x - 3y = 3 \\ -5x - 17 = y \end{cases}$

14) $\begin{cases} y = -3x + 5 \\ 5x - 4y = -3 \end{cases}$

15) $\begin{cases} y - 5x = -7 \\ 12 - 2y = 3x \end{cases}$

16) $\begin{cases} y = 6 + 4x \\ -5x - y = 21 \end{cases}$

17) $\begin{cases} -7x - 2y = -13 \\ x - 2y = 11 \end{cases}$

18) $\begin{cases} -5x + y = -2 \\ 12 + 6y = 3x \end{cases}$

19) $\begin{cases} 3 + y - 5x = 0 \\ 3x - 8y = 24 \end{cases}$

20) $\begin{cases} x + 3y = 1 \\ -3x - 3y = -15 \end{cases}$

21) $\begin{cases} -3x - 8y = 20 \\ -5x + y = 19 \end{cases}$

22) $\begin{cases} 3y - 3x = 3 \\ y - 5x = 13 \end{cases}$

23) $\begin{cases} 6x + 6y = -6 \\ 5x + y = -13 \end{cases}$

24) $\begin{cases} 2x + y = 20 \\ 6x - 5y = 12 \end{cases}$

25) $\begin{cases} -3x - 4y = 2 \\ 3x + 3y = -3 \end{cases}$

26) $\begin{cases} -2x + 6y = 6 \\ -7x + 8y = -5 \end{cases}$

27) $\begin{cases} 4x + y = 24 \\ y = 4x + 24 \end{cases}$

28) $\begin{cases} -5x + 2y = 9 \\ y = 7x \end{cases}$

29) $\begin{cases} -7x - 6y - 4 = 0 \\ x - 8 = -3y \end{cases}$

30) $\begin{cases} -4x = 20 - 7y \\ y = 3x + 15 \end{cases}$

Solving Systems of Equations by Elimination

✎Solve each system of equation by elimination.

1) $\begin{cases} -4x - 2y = -12 \\ 4x + 8y = -24 \end{cases}$

2) $\begin{cases} 4x + 8y = 20 \\ -4x + 2y = -30 \end{cases}$

3) $\begin{cases} x - y = 11 \\ 2x + y = 19 \end{cases}$

4) $\begin{cases} -6x + 5y = 1 \\ 6x + 4y = -10 \end{cases}$

5) $\begin{cases} -2x + 9y = -25 \\ -4x - 9y = -23 \end{cases}$

6) $\begin{cases} 8x + y = -16 \\ -3x + y = -5 \end{cases}$

7) $\begin{cases} -6x + 6y = 6 \\ -6x + 3y = -12 \end{cases}$

8) $\begin{cases} 7x + 2y = 24 \\ 8x + 2y = 30 \end{cases}$

9) $\begin{cases} 5x + y = 9 \\ 10x - 7y = -18 \end{cases}$

10) $\begin{cases} -4x + 9y = 9 \\ x - 3y = -6 \end{cases}$

11) $\begin{cases} -3x + 7y = -16 \\ -9x + 5y = 16 \end{cases}$

12) $\begin{cases} -7x + y = -19 \\ -2x + 3y = -19 \end{cases}$

13) $\begin{cases} 16x - 10y = 10 \\ -8x - 6y = 6 \end{cases}$

14) $\begin{cases} 8x + 14y = 4 \\ -6x - 7y = -10 \end{cases}$

15) $\begin{cases} -4x - 15y = -17 \\ -x + 5y = -13 \end{cases}$

16) $\begin{cases} -x - 7y = 14 \\ -4x - 14y = 28 \end{cases}$

17) $\begin{cases} -7x - 8y = 9 \\ -4x + 9y = -22 \end{cases}$

18) $\begin{cases} 5x + 4y = -30 \\ 3x - 9y = -18 \end{cases}$

19) $\begin{cases} -4x - 2y = 14 \\ -10x + 7y = -25 \end{cases}$

20) $\begin{cases} 3x - 2y = 2 \\ 5x - 5y = 10 \end{cases}$

21) $\begin{cases} 5x + 4y = -14 \\ 3x + 6y = 6 \end{cases}$

22) $\begin{cases} 2x + 10y = 6 \\ -5x - 20y = -15 \end{cases}$

23) $\begin{cases} -7x - 20y = -14 \\ 10y + 4 = 2x \end{cases}$

24) $\begin{cases} 3 + 2x = y \\ -3 - 7y = 10x \end{cases}$

25) $\begin{cases} -10x + 3y = 5 \\ x - y = -4 \end{cases}$

26) $\begin{cases} 12x - 5y = -20 \\ y = x + 4 \end{cases}$

27) $\begin{cases} -4x + 11y = 15 \\ x - 2y = 0 \end{cases}$

28) $\begin{cases} 7x - 3y = 20 \\ y = 5x - 4 \end{cases}$

29) $\begin{cases} -5x + 4y = 3 \\ x + 15 = 2y \end{cases}$

30) $\begin{cases} 8x + 5y = 24 \\ y = -4x \end{cases}$

Systems of Equations Word Problems

✎ *Solve.*

1) A used book store also started selling used CDs and videos. In the first week, the store sold a combination of 40 CDs and videos. They charged $4 per CD and $6 per video and the total sales were $180. Determine the total number of CDs and videos sold.

2) At the end of the 2000-2001 football season, 31 Super Bowl games had been played with the current two football leagues, the American Football Conference (AFC) and the National Football Conference (NFC). The NFC won five more games than the AFC. Determine the total number of wins by each conference.

3) The length of Sally's garden is 4 meters greater than 3 times the width. The perimeter of her garden is 72 meters. Find the dimensions of Sally's garden.

4) Giselle works as a carpenter and as a blacksmith. She earns $20 as a carpenter and $25 as a blacksmith. Last week, Giselle worked both jobs for a total of 30 hours and earned a total of $690. How long did Giselle work as a carpenter last week, and how long did she work as a blacksmith?

5) At a sale on winter clothing, Cody bought two pairs of gloves and four hats for $43.00. Tori bought two pairs of gloves and two hats for $30.00. Find the prices of the hats and gloves.

Answers of Worksheets

Solving Systems of Equations by Substitution

1) $(-1,3)$
2) $(4,-6)$
3) $(2,1)$
4) $(-5,3)$
5) $(4,6)$
6) $(4,-8)$
7) $(-3,-5)$
8) $(-2,7)$

9) $(1,-3)$
10) $(0,0)$
11) $(2,1)$
12) $(4,3)$
13) $(-4,3)$
14) $(1,2)$
15) $(2,3)$
16) $(-3,-6)$

17) $(3,-4)$
18) $(0,-2)$
19) $(0,-3)$
20) $(7,-2)$
21) $(-4,-1)$
22) $(-3,-2)$
23) $(-3,2)$
24) $(7,6)$

25) $(-2,1)$
26) $(3,2)$
27) $(0,24)$
28) $(1,7)$
29) $(-4,4)$
30) $(-5,0)$

Solving Systems of Equations by Elimination

1) $(6,-6)$
2) $(7,-1)$
3) $(10,-1)$
4) $(-1,-1)$
5) $(8,-1)$
6) $(-1,-8)$
7) $(5,6)$
8) $(6,-9)$

9) $(1,4)$
10) $(9,5)$
11) $(-4,-4)$
12) $(2,-5)$
13) $(0,-1)$
14) $(4,-2)$
15) $(8,-1)$
16) $(0,-2)$

17) $(1,-2)$
18) $(-6,0)$
19) $(-1,-5)$
20) $(-2,-4)$
21) $(-6,4)$
22) $(3,0)$
23) $(2,0)$
24) $(-1,1)$

25) $(1,5)$
26) $(0,4)$
27) $(10,5)$
28) $(-1,-9)$
29) $(9,12)$
30) $(-2,8)$

Systems of Equations Word Problems

1) $(10\ videos, 30 CDs)$
2) $(NFC\ wins\ 18, AFC\ wins 13)$
3) $(8,28)$

4) $(12,18)$
5) $(gloves: \$6, hats: \$8.5)$

Chapter 8:

Linear Functions

Topics that you'll learn in this part:

- ✓ Finding Slope
- ✓ Graphing Lines Using Slope–Intercept Form
- ✓ Graphing Lines Using Standard Form
- ✓ Writing Linear Equations
- ✓ Graphing Linear Inequalities
- ✓ Finding Midpoint
- ✓ Finding Distance of Two Points
- ✓ Slope and Rate of Change
- ✓ Find the Slope, X–intercept and Y–intercept
- ✓ Write an Equation from a Graph
- ✓ Slope–intercept form
- ✓ Point–slope form
- ✓ Equations of horizontal and vertical lines
- ✓ Equation of parallel or perpendicular lines

Finding Slope

✍️ *Find the slope of the line through each pair of points.*

1) $(0, 2), (-3, 2)$

2) $(2, 2), (-3, -2)$

3) $(0, 0), (4, -2)$

4) $(2, 5), (1, 1)$

5) $(15, 8), (15, -8)$

6) $(-2, 0), (1, 3)$

7) $(-2, -4), (2, 3)$

8) $(-2, -4), (-1, 0)$

9) $(-6, 5), (-1, 0)$

10) $(-6, 10), (4, 0)$

11) $(15, 5), (-5, 1)$

12) $(-10, -2), (0, 3)$

13) $(5, -2), (3, 3)$

14) $(5, 0), (10, 10)$

15) $(0, 2), (2, 10)$

16) $(0, 0), (-10, 10)$

17) $(-22, -12), (-5, 5)$

18) $(0, 0), (-10, 30)$

19) $(12, 12), (-3, 6)$

20) $(-6, 2), (-4, 6)$

21) $(-2, 7), (-8, 7)$

22) $(14, 70), (28, 7)$

23) $(9, 6), (-1, -1)$

24) $(0, 6), (12, 24)$

✍️ *Solve.*

25) Some building codes require the slope of a stairway to be no steeper than 0.88 or $\frac{22}{25}$. The stairs in the Adam's house measure 11-inch-deep and 6 inch high. Do the stairs meet the code requirement?

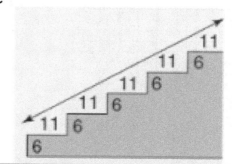

Graphing Lines Using Slope–Intercept Form

✍️ *Sketch the graph of each line.*

1) $y = \frac{1}{2}x - 4$

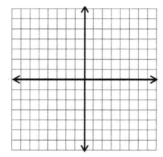

2) $y = x + 1$

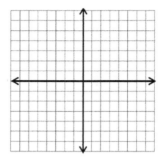

3) $y = -x + 1$

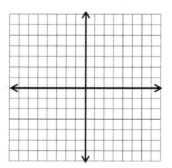

4) $y = 3x - 1$

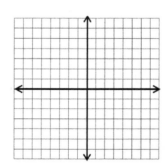

5) $y = -\frac{1}{5}x + \frac{1}{3}$

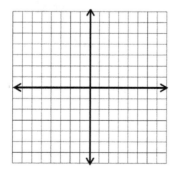

6) $y = \frac{3}{5}x - 1$

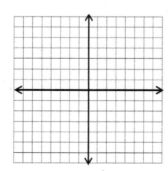

Graphing Lines Using Standard Form

✍ *Sketch the graph of each line.*

1) $2x - 2y = 4$

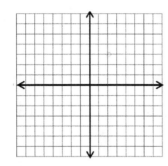

2) $3x + y = 2$

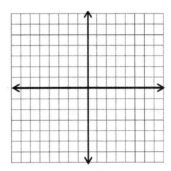

3) $x - y = 10$

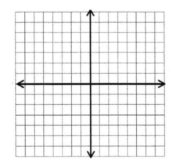

4) $3x + 2y = 2$

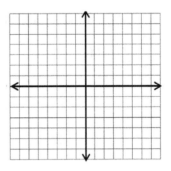

5) $y - 2x = 6$

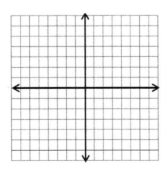

6) $2x - 3y = 6$

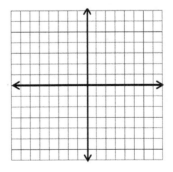

Writing Linear Equations

📐*Write the slope–intercept form of the equation of the line through the given points.*

1) through: $(0, 2), (2, 4)$
2) through: $(0, 1), (2, -3)$
3) through: $(0, 2), (-2, -4)$
4) through: $(0, 2), (2, -8)$
5) through: $(0, 4), (-8, 0)$
6) through: $(1, 0), (0, -3)$
7) through: $(0, -2), (3, 0)$
8) through: $(0, 1), (-1, -3)$
9) through: $(1, -1), (1, 5)$
10) through: $(0, -0.5), (2, 3.5)$

11) through: $(0, 5), (-3, -4)$
12) through: $(5, 0), (0, 5)$
13) through: $(1, -6), (1.5, 0)$
14) through: $(0, 2), (1, -7)$
15) through: $(0, 3), (3, -3)$
16) through: $(0, 6), (5, -4)$
17) through: $(0, 3), (2, -5)$
18) through: $(4, 3), (2, 6)$
19) through: $(0, 1), (-4, 11)$
20) through: $(1.5, 2), (4, 5.5)$

📐*Write the line slope from graph.*

21)

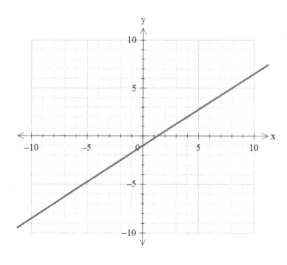

22)

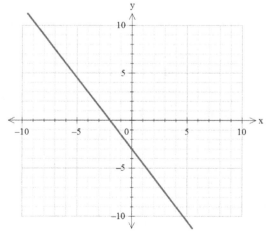

Graphing Linear Inequalities

🖎 *Sketch the graph of each linear inequality.*

1) $y > 3x + 4$

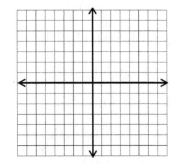

2) $y < -2x - 1$

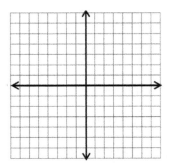

3) $y + \frac{1}{2} \geq \frac{1}{2}x$

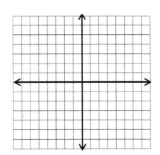

4) $y \leq 3 - 2x$

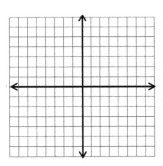

5) $4x - 2 \leq y$

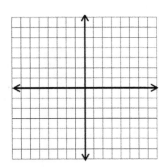

6) $1 - y \geq x$

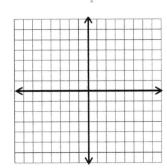

Finding Midpoint

✎ *Find the midpoint of the line segment with the given endpoints.*

1) $(-4, 5), (3, -\frac{1}{2})$

2) $(3, 7), (5, -3)$

3) $(-4, -2), (1, -10)$

4) $(3, -\frac{3}{2}), (4, 2)$

5) $(7, 0), (0, -10)$

6) $(4, -9), (0, 0)$

7) $(-3, -10), (3, 3)$

8) $(9, 1), (4, 4)$

9) $(75, 80), (40, 0)$

10) $(0, 13), (13, 0)$

11) $(-10, -3), (15, 14)$

12) $(33, 13), (9, 11)$

13) $(15, 0), (-10, -1)$

14) $(-3, 3), (15, 20)$

15) $(1, 10), (33, 0.5)$

16) $(90, -90), (50, 0)$

✎ *Solve.*

17) Find the midpoint of $\overline{AB}$ using the information in the diagram.

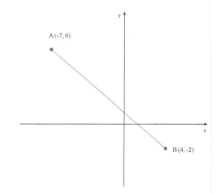

18) See the diagram. Find the midpoint of $\overline{BC}$.

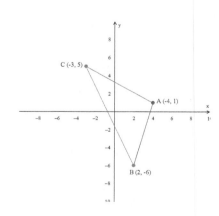

Finding Distance of Two Points

✏ *Find the distance between each pair of points.*

1) $(5, 7), (5, 3)$

2) $(6, 0), (-4, -10)$

3) $(-2, 1), (10, -5)$

4) $(33, -5), (17, 8)$

5) $(-6, -5), (6, 5)$

6) $(0, 0), (5, 8)$

7) $(3, 4), (0, 0)$

8) $(12, 16) (0, 0)$

9) $(-17, 1), (2, -6)$

10) $(-3, 0), (14, 0)$

✏ *Solve.*

11) Camp Sunshine is also on the lake. Use the Pythagorean Theorem to find the distance between Gabriela's house and Camp Sunshine to the nearest tenth of a meter.

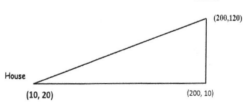

Camp
sunrise

(200,120)

House

(10, 20)   (200, 10)

12) The class of math is mapped on a coordinate grid with the origin being at the center point of the hall. Mary's seat is located at the point (-4, 7) and Betty's seat is located at (-2, 5). How far is it from Mary's seat to Betty's seat?

13) The teaching building of a university is mapped on a coordinate grid with the origin being at library. Math's building is located at the point (1,5) and History's building is located at (4, 9). How far is it from Math's building to History's building?

Slope and Rate of Change

✏️ *Find the slope of the line that passes through the points.*

1) $(-10, 4), (0, 2)$

2) $(3, 1), (12,0)$

3) $(15, 0), (2, 13)$

4) $(12, 97), (-3, -5)$

5) $(-10, -8), (3, 1)$

6) $(-17, 20), (-1, -1)$

7) $(-2, -2), (0, 8)$

8) $(15, -8), (-1, 8)$

9) $(13,0), (-3,11)$

10) $(4,3), (5,1)$

11) $(12,3), (-4,3)$

12) $(1, -1), (0,0)$

✏️ *Find the value of* r *so the line that passes through each pair of points*

has the given slope.

13) $(1, 1), (2, r), m = 2$

14) $(-1, r), (0, 3), m = 1$

15) $(3, -1), (r, 3), m = -4$

16) $(r, -1), (0, 5), m = 3$

17) $(5, 1), (2, r), m = -1$

18) $(-3,1), (r, 4), m = 3$

19) $(6, 2), (r, 4), m = 2$

20) $(6, r), (3, 4), m = -3$

21) $(12, -9), (r, -8), m = -1$

22) $(7, r), (5, -2), m = 3$

23) $(1, 1), (r, 5), m = 2$

24) $(7, r), (5, 10), m = -11$

25) $(1, 1), (r, 5), m = 2$

26) $(4, r), (-3, -8), m = \frac{2}{7}$

27) $(7, -12), (5, r), m = -11$

28) $(19, 3), (20, r), m = 0$

29) $(15, 8), (r, 9), m = -\frac{1}{32}$

30) $(r, -12), (15, -3), m = 1$

31) $(3, 1), (r, -5), m = -\frac{3}{2}$

32) $(3, -2), (-7, r), m = -1$

33) $(20, r), (-20, -10), m = 0.875$

34) $(6,0), (r, -2), m = 0.2$

35) $(200,100), (100, r), m = -1$

36) $(0, r), (10,0), m = -0.5$

37) $(2, -8), (-10, r), m = -0.5$

Find the Slope, x–intercept and y–intercept

✎ *Find the* x *and* y *intercepts for the following equations.*

1) $x + 2y = -2$

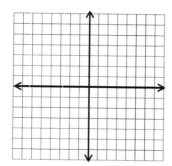

2) $y = 2x - 3$

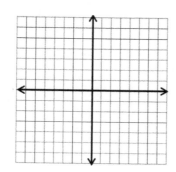

3) $-3x = 3y + 1$

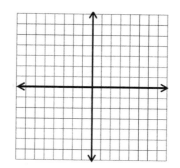

4) $2 - 2y = -5x$

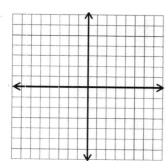

5) $-5x + 2y = 10$

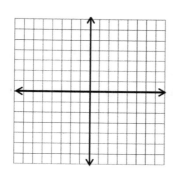

6) $2y = 2 - x$

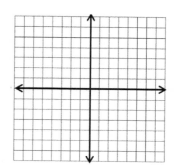

7) $1 - 2y = 7x$

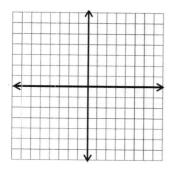

8) $2x + 4y = 9$

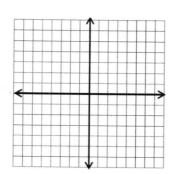

9) $3y = 7 + 2x$

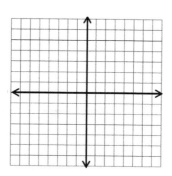

Write an equation from a graph

✍️ *Write the slope intercept form of the equation of each line.*

1)

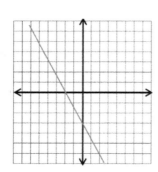

2)

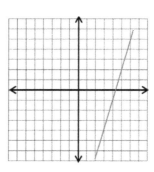

3)

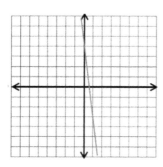

4)

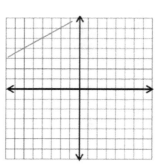

5)

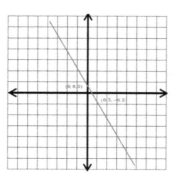

6)

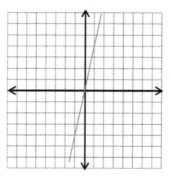

Slope–intercept Form

✍ *Write the slope–intercept form of the equation of each line.*

1) $3x - 12 = 12y$

2) $2x - 3y = 6$

3) $\frac{-3}{2}x + 5y = 5$

4) $3(2x + y) = 6$

5) $14x + 7y = 28$

6) $3x - 4y = 5y + 1$

7) $3x + 4y = 3 + y$

8) $4 - 2x + y = 2$

9) $3x - y = 2$

10) $4y - 5x = -5$

11) $7x + 4y = 14 - 3y$

12) $15y - 5x = 30$

✍ *Solve.*

13) Suppose that the water level of a river is 34 feet and that it is receding at a rate of 0.5 foot per day. Find the slope and write a sentence to interpret the slope in detail. Write an equation for the water level, L, after d days. In how many days will the water level be 26 feet?

14) For babysitting, Nicole charges a flat fee of $3, plus $5 per hour. Write an equation for the cost, C, after h hours of babysitting. What do you think the slope and the y-intercept represent? How much money will she make if she baby-sits 5 hours?

15) In order to "curve" a set of test scores, a teacher uses the equation $y = 2.5x + 10$, where y is the curved test score and x is the number of problems answered correctly. Find the test score of a student who answers 32 problems correctly. Explain what the slope and the y-intercept mean in the equation.

Point–slope Form

✎ *Find the slope of the following lines. Name a point on each line.*

1) $y = 3(x + 3)$

2) $y = 3x - 2$

3) $y = 4x + 3$

4) $y = \frac{2}{3}x - 1$

5) $y + 3 = 4x + 8$

6) $2y = 3x - 4$

7) $y - 1 = 4x - 2$

8) $3y - 4 = 2x$

9) $y + 1 = 3x - 3$

10) $4y - 8 = 4x + 10$

11) $y + 1 = 32(x + 1)$

12) $15x + 3 = 3y$

✎ *Write an equation in point–slope form for the line that passes through the given point with the slope provided.*

13) $(3,2), m = \frac{1}{2}$

14) $(1,-2), m = 3$

15) $(3,-2), m = -2$

16) $(4,1), m = 3$

17) $(-2,-3), m = -\frac{1}{2}$

18) $\left(\frac{3}{4}, -\frac{1}{2}\right), m = 3$

19) $(-2,0) m = \frac{3}{4}$

20) $\left(-\frac{3}{7}, \frac{1}{2}\right), m = 2$

21) $(0,2), m = 5$

22) $(-3,1), m = \frac{4}{5}$

23) $\left(-\frac{2}{3}, \frac{2}{3}\right), m = 4$

24) $(5,0), m = \frac{1}{5}$

25) $(3,3), m = 10$

26) $(-6,-5), m = -1$

27) $(-6,0), m = -\frac{2}{3}$

28) $(1,1), m = -4$

29) $(-3,2), m = -4$

30) $\left(-\frac{1}{2}, \frac{1}{4}\right), m = \frac{1}{2}$

31) $(-4,2), m = \frac{7}{3}$

32) $(0,1), m = \frac{1}{2}$

33) $(4,1), m = 2$

34) $(3,3), m = -1$

35) $(-1,0), m = -2$

36) $(6,5), m = 4$

37) $(1,-2), m = 3$

Equations of Horizontal and Vertical Lines

✍️ *Sketch the graph of each line.*

1) $y = 0$

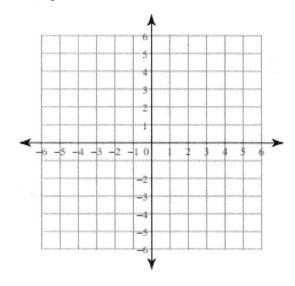

2) $y = 2$

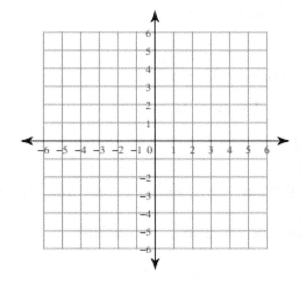

3) $x = -4$

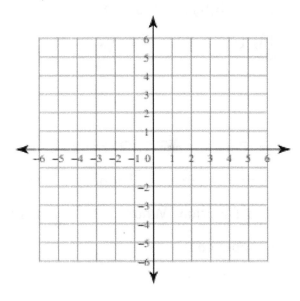

4) $x = 3$

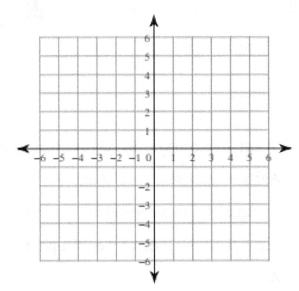

Equation of Parallel or Perpendicular Lines

✍ *Write an equation of the line that passes through the given point and is parallel to the given line.*

1) $(-2,3), 2y + 1 = 3x$

2) $(0,7), 3y + x = 2$

3) $(6, -1), 3y - x = 1$

4) $(-2,4), y + 2x = 2$

5) $(3,2), 2y + x = -2$

6) $(1,6) - 2y = x + 1$

7) $(3,2), y = 1 - x$

8) $(2,2), y = 3x$

9) $(-3,0), y = 2x - 2$

10) $(-3,2), 3y - 2 = 3x$

✍ *Write an equation of the line that passes through the given point and is perpendicular to the given line.*

11) $(-2,1), y + 1 = 3x$

12) $(0, -7), y + 2x = 2$

13) $(0, -1), 2y - 2x = 1$

14) $(-3,3), 2y + 2x = 2$

15) $(5,0), 3x + y = 5$

16) $(1,2), y = 3x + 1$

17) $(-3,0), 2y + 3 = x$

18) $(4,3), y = -5x + 1$

✍ *Solve.*

19) A caterer charges $120 to cater a party for 15 people and $200 for 25 people. Assume that the cost, y, is a linear function of the number of x people. Write an equation in slope-intercept form for this function. What does the slope represent? How much would a party for 40 people cost?

A. $280

B. $330

C. $300

D. $320

Answers of Worksheets

Finding Slope

1) 0	6) 1	11) 0.2	16) −1	21) 0
2) 0.8	7) 1.75	12) 0.5	17) 1	22) −4.5
3) −0.5	8) 4	13) −2.5	18) −3	23) 0.7
4) 4	9) −1	14) 2	19) 0.4	24) 1.5
5) Undefined	10) −1	15) 4	20) 2	25) 2.5

Graphing Lines Using Slope–Intercept Form

1)

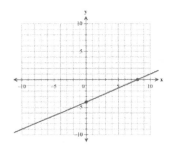

2)

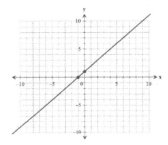

3)

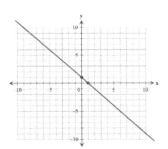

4)

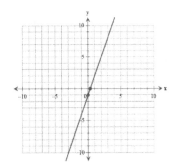

5)

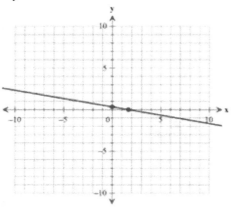

6)

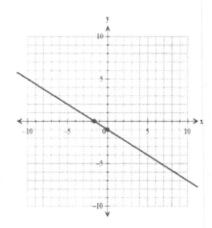

Graphing Lines Using Standard Form

1)

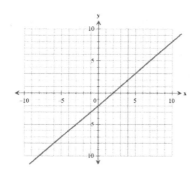

2)

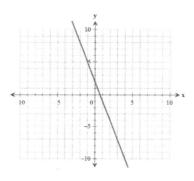

3)

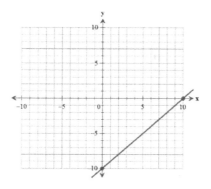

4)

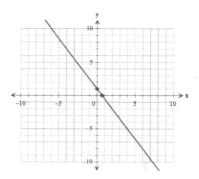

5)

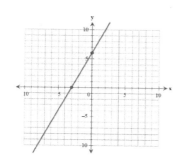

6)

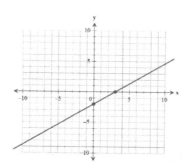

Writing Linear Equations

1) $y = x + 2$

2) $y = 1 - 2x$

3) $y = 3x + 2$

4) $y = 2 - 5x$

5) $y = \frac{1}{2}x + 4$

6) $y = 3x - 3$

7) $y = \frac{2}{3}x - 2$

8) $y = 4x + 1$

9) $x = 1$

10) $y = 2x - \frac{1}{2}$

11) $y = 3x + 5$

12) $y = -x + 5$

13) $y = 12x - 18$

14) $y = -9x + 2$

15) $y = 3 - 2x$

16) $y = 6 - 2x$

17) $y = 3 - 4x$

18) $y = 9 - \frac{3}{2}x$

19) $y = 1 - 2\frac{1}{2}x$

20) $y = 1.4x - 0.1$

21) $y = 0.75x - 1$

22) $y = -1.5x - 3$

Graphing Linear Inequalities

1)

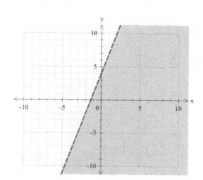

2)

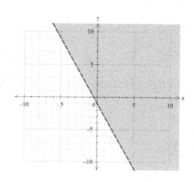

3)

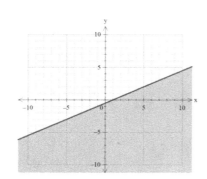

4)

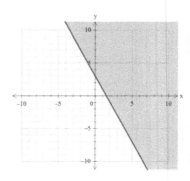

5)

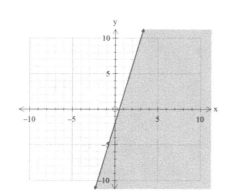

6)

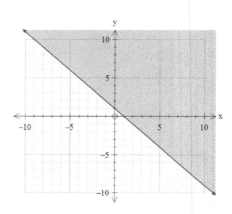

Finding Midpoint

1) $(-0.5, 2.25)$ 6) $(2, -4.5)$ 11) $(2.5, 5.5)$ 16) $(70, -45)$

2) $(4, 2)$ 7) $(0, -3.5)$ 12) $(21, 12)$ 17) $(-1.5, 2)$

3) $(-1.5, -6)$ 8) $(6.5, 2.5)$ 13) $(2.5, -0.5)$ 18) $(-0.5, -0.5)$

4) $(3.5, 0.25)$ 9) $(57.5, 40)$ 14) $(6, 11.5)$

5) $(3.5, -5)$ 10) $(6.5, 6.5)$ 15) $(17, 5.25)$

Finding Distance of Two Points

1) 4   4) 20.62   7) 5   10) 17   13) 5

2) 14.14   5) 15.62   8) 20   11) 214.7

3) 13.41   6) 9.43   9) 20.25   12) $2\sqrt{2}$

Slope and Rate of Change

1) -0.2

2) $-\frac{1}{9}$

3) -1

4) $\frac{34}{5}$

5) $\frac{9}{13}$

6) $-\frac{7}{2}$

7) 5

8) -1

9) $-\frac{11}{16}$

10) -2

11) 0

12) -1

13) 3

14) 2

15) 2

16) -2

17) 4

18) -2

19) 7

20) -5

21) 11

22) 4

23) 3

24) -12

25) 3

26) -6

27) 10

28) 3

29) -17

30) 6

31) 7

32) 8

33) 25

34) -4

35) 200

36) 5

37) -2

Find the Slope, $x-$ intercept and y$-$intercept

1) $y = -1, x = -2$

2) $y = -3, x = \frac{3}{2}$

3) $y = -\frac{1}{3}, x = -\frac{1}{3}$

4) $y = 1, x = -\frac{2}{5}$

5) $y = 5, x = -2$

6) $y = 1, x = 2$

7) $y = \frac{1}{2}, x = 2$

8) $y = \frac{9}{4}, x = \frac{9}{2}$

9) $y = \frac{7}{3}, x = -\frac{7}{2}$

Write an equation from a graph

1) $y = -\frac{3}{2}x - 3$

2) $y = 3x - 13$

3) $y = -7x + 4$

4) $y = \frac{1}{2}x + 7$

5) $y = -2x + \frac{1}{2}$

6) $y = 4x$

Slope–intercept form

1) $y = \frac{1}{4}x - 4$

2) $y = \frac{2}{3}x - 2$

3) $y = \frac{3}{10}x + 1$

4) $y = -2x + 2$

5) $y = -2x + 4$

6) $y = \frac{1}{3}x - \frac{1}{9}$

7) $y = -x + 1$

8) $y = 2x - 2$

9) $y = 3x - 2$

10) $y = \frac{5}{x}x - \frac{5}{4}$

11) $y = -x + 2$

12) $y = \frac{1}{3}x + 2$

13) $l = 34 - \frac{1}{2}d, 16\ days$

14) 28

15) 90

Point–slope form

1) $m = 3, (-3, 0)$

2) $m = 3, \left(\frac{2}{3}, 0\right)$

3) $m = 4, (-3, -9)$

4) $m = \frac{2}{3}, (0, -1)$

5) $m = 4, (-2, -3)$

6) $m = \frac{3}{2}, (0, -2)$

7) $m = 4, \left(\frac{1}{2}, 1\right)$

8) $m = \frac{2}{3}, \left(0, \frac{4}{3}\right)$

9) $m = 3, (1, -1)$

10) $m = 1, \left(-\frac{10}{4}, 2\right)$

11) $m = 32, (-1, -1)$

12) $m = 5, (-1, -2)$

13) $y = \frac{1}{2}x + 1$

14) $y = 3x - 5$

15) $y = -2x + 4$

16) $y = 3x - 11$

17) $y = -\frac{1}{2}x - 4$

18) $y = 3x - \frac{11}{4}$

19) $y = -\frac{3}{4}x - \frac{3}{2}$

20) $y = 2x + \frac{19}{14}$

21) $y = 5x + 2$

22) $y = \frac{4}{5}x + \frac{17}{5}$

23) $y = 4x + \frac{25}{6}$

24) $y = \frac{1}{5}x - 1$

25) $y = 10x - 37$

26) $y = -x - 11$

27) $y = -\frac{2}{3}x - 4$

28) $y = -4x + 5$

29) $y = -4x - 10$

30) $y = \frac{1}{2}x + \frac{1}{2}$

31) $y = \frac{7}{3}x + \frac{34}{3}$

32) $y = \frac{1}{2}x + 1$

33) $y = 2x - 7$

34) $y = -x$

35) $y = -2x - 2$

36) $y = 4x - 19$

37) $y = 3x - 5$

Equations of horizontal and vertical lines

1) $y = 0$ (it is on x axes)

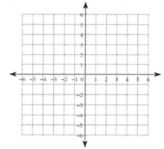

2) $y = 2$

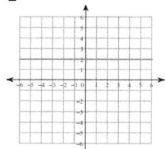

3) $x = -4$

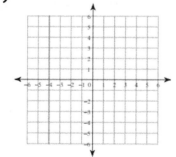

4) $x = 3$

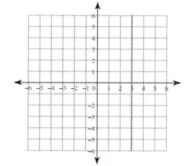

Equation of parallel or perpendicular lines

1) $y = \frac{3}{2}x + 6$

2) $y = -\frac{1}{3}x + 7$

3) $y = \frac{1}{3}x - 3$

4) $y = -2x$

5) $y = -\frac{1}{2}x + \frac{7}{2}$

6) $y = -\frac{1}{2}x + \frac{13}{2}$

7) $y = -x + 5$

8) $y = 3x - 4$

9) $y = x + 6$

10) $y = x + 5$

11) $y = -\frac{1}{3}x + \frac{1}{3}$

12) $y = \frac{1}{2}x - 7$

13) $y = -x$

14) $y = x + 6$

15) $y = \frac{1}{3}x - \frac{5}{3}$

16) $y = -\frac{1}{3}x + \frac{7}{3}$

17) $y = -2x - 6$

18) $y = \frac{1}{5}x + \frac{11}{5}$

19) $Y = 8x, \$32$

Chapter 9:

Monomials and Polynomials

Topics that you'll learn in this part:

- ✓ Classifying Polynomials
- ✓ Writing Polynomials in Standard Form
- ✓ Simplifying Polynomials
- ✓ Add and Subtract Monomials
- ✓ Multiplying Monomials
- ✓ Multiplying and Dividing Monomials
- ✓ GCF of Monomials
- ✓ Powers of Monomials
- ✓ Multiplying a Polynomial and a Monomial
- ✓ Multiplying Binomials
- ✓ Factoring Trinomials

Writing Polynomials in Standard Form

✍ *Write each polynomial in standard form.*

1) $3x^2 - 4x^3 + 1 =$

2) $7x - x^3 + 5x^2 =$

3) $15x + x^3 =$

4) $2(x^2 + 1) + x^4 =$

5) $(x - 1)x + 1) =$

6) $x(3x + 7) - x^4 =$

7) $15x - 4x^2 - 7x + 3 =$

8) $3(x - 2) - x^3 =$

9) $6x(x - 4) + 4x^2 + 1 =$

10) $3x^2 - 4x - 2(x^2 + 1) =$

11) $4x^3 + 2x - 5x^5 =$

12) $2 - 4x - 2(x^2 + 1) =$

13) $3x + (x + 1)(x + 1) =$

14) $4x - 5x^3 + 4 =$

15) $14y - 3y^2 + 2y =$

16) $4m(m^2 - 1) + 3m^4 =$

17) $2x - 4x^2 - 7x - 3x =$

18) $7x^3 + \frac{x^3 + x^2}{x^2} =$

19) $\frac{4N^4 + 4N}{2N} + N^2 =$

20) $17x^2 - 4x^5 + x^{10} =$

21) $-3x^5 + 4x - 9x^2 =$

22) $2x(x + 1) + \frac{3x + x^2}{x} =$

23) $17x - 4x^3 + 5x^2 + 1 =$

24) $(-3)\frac{x^2 - 9x + 15x^3}{3x} + x^3 =$

25) $14x^5 + \frac{x^5 + x^4}{2x^2} =$

26) $12x - 4 + 4x^3 + x^2 =$

27) $4x^3 + 7x^2 + 28x^5 =$

28) $34x^4 - 2x + 7x^2 =$

29) $2x^2(x^2 + 4x) + x =$

30) $-3x^2 + 4x - 7x^3 =$

31) $25x\left(\frac{1}{5}x^2 - \frac{x}{2}\right) =$

32) $x^2 + 4x^5 + x^3 =$

33) $2x^2 - 3x - 7x^2 - x =$

34) $2x^2 - 4x^4 + x^2 =$

35) $-3x + 7x^2 - x(x + 1) =$

36) $5x - x^2 + x^5 + x^3 =$

37) $4 + 2x - x^2 =$

38) $2z - 3 + z^3 =$

39) $p^6 - 2 + 3p^3 =$

40) $2y - 2y^6 + y^4 =$

41) $9x + x^2 - 7 =$

42) $2x + 1 =$

43) $3z^3 + 5 =$

44) $2 - 3q + q^2$

Simplifying Polynomials

✍ *Simplify each expression.*

1) $(-5)(4m^2 - 5m - 8)$

2) $2d(d^5 - 7d^3 + 4)$

3) $7rs(4r^2 + 9s^3 - 7rs)$

4) $8x^4(6x - 8x^3 + 7)$

5) $(y + 3)(y + 5)$

6) $(2x + 4)(x + 9)$

7) $(4b - 3)(4b + 3)$

8) $(n + 4m)(2n - 3m)$

9) $(x + 4)(6x^2 + 2x - 8)$

10) $(4z + 6)(4z + 6)$

11) $(x - 2)(9 - 5x)$

12) $(4b - 3)(4b - 3)$

13) $(3x^2 - 2x)(7x - 8x^2 - 9)$

✍ *Solve.*

14) Find the perimeter of the triangle pictured.

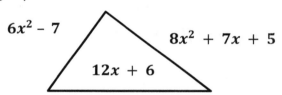

$6x^2 - 7$ $8x^2 + 7x + 5$

$12x + 6$

15) Find the area of the rectangles pictured.

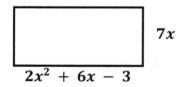

$7x$

$2x^2 + 6x - 3$

16) A triangle has sides of length $3x + 4y$, $5y + 6 + 2x$, and $7 + 8x$. What is the perimeter of the triangle?

17) Triangle has a perimeter $10x^2 - 3xy - 6y^2$. If two sides are known to be $2x^2 + 2xy$ and $7x^2 + 3y^2$, then what is the length of the third unknown side?

Add and Subtract monomials

✍ *Find each sum and difference.*

1) $3x^3y - 12x^3y =$

2) $10(3uv - u) + 5u =$

3) $12x^2z - z(5x^2 - z) =$

4) $3x^2(z + y) - 2x^2z =$

5) $14(x^2yz^2 - x) + x^2yz^2 + 12x =$

6) $6\frac{x^2}{y} - 4\frac{x^2}{y} =$

7) $3\left(x^2 + \frac{1}{y}\right) - x^2 + \frac{2}{y} =$

8) $3x^2z + (x^2)(2z) =$

9) $3\frac{z}{y}x^2 + 2x^2\left(1 + \frac{z}{y}\right) - x^2 =$

10) $3uvw - 15uvw =$

11) $12ux^2 - 14ux^2 =$

12) $3x(x^2 + y) + x^3 - 4xy =$

13) $3y^2zx^2 + 17x^2(zy^2 + 1) =$

14) $10m^6 + 12m^6 - 14m^6 =$

15) $32e^{-i\omega t} - 18e^{-i\omega t} =$

16) $15lq - 5lq + lq =$

17) $\frac{xyz}{2} + \frac{3}{2}xyz =$

18) $95\,lqr - 39lqr =$

19) $33\frac{z^3x}{y} - 19\frac{z^3x}{y} =$

20) $7(x^2z - y) + x^2z =$

21) $x^2zy - 2x^2(1 - zy) + 2x^2 =$

22) $33(x^2 + rs) - 30x^2 - 45rs =$

23) $12z^3x - 18z^3x =$

24) $x^2(yz) + 12x^2(yz) =$

25) $4xy - 15xy =$

26) $-2x^2y + x^2y - 3x^2y =$

27) $3\frac{x^2}{z} + 10\frac{x^2}{z} - 2\frac{x^2}{z} =$

28) $4yzu - 12yzu =$

29) $12ut - 14ut - 33ut =$

30) $15frq + 3frq =$

31) $12(x - yz) + 12x - 9yz =$

32) $10(x^2 - 2y) + 18y =$

33) $3\frac{xyz}{t} + 4\frac{xyz}{t} =$

34) $33(t^2e^{-i\omega t}) - (40t^2e^{-i\omega t}) =$

35) $\frac{t^3x}{z} + 4\left(\frac{t^3x}{z} - x\right) + 3x =$

36) $5wt - 12wt - 33wt =$

37) $2x + \frac{(x+1)^2}{x+1} =$

38) $3x^3 - 2x - 4x^3 + x =$

39) $2z^2 - 4z - 3z^2 =$

40) $\frac{(3x+1)(3x-1)}{3x-1} + x =$

41) $9r - 3r^2 - 8r =$

42) $3t(t + 1) - 3t =$

Multiplying Monomials

✎ *Simplify each expression.*

1) $(2x)(2x)^3 =$

2) $(2n^5)(n^2)^2 =$

3) $\left(\frac{x^2}{2}\right)^5 (3x) =$

4) $\left(\frac{2b}{3}\right)^4 (3b) =$

5) $-2x\left(\frac{1}{2x^2}\right)^4 =$

6) $(x\left(\frac{1}{2}x\right)^2)^3 =$

7) $5x^2z(2z) =$

8) $12xyz(x^2z) =$

9) $x^2y(12xz) =$

10) $3x^2z^3(2yzx) =$

11) $7(x^2zt)(t^2zx) =$

12) $(-2u^3vw)(4vw) =$

13) $(-5)(mn^3)(3nm^2)(mn) =$

14) $2(x^2y)(yz)(zxy) =$

15) $3v^2(9uw)(vw)^5 =$

16) $6(x^5)(xz^4)(zxy) =$

17) $(3c^3b)(b^2a)(cb) =$

18) $14x(3xz)(2yz) =$

19) $x^2(3yzx)(z^3xy) =$

20) $-5z^4(y^5z)(3xz) =$

21) $3(u^3v)(uv^3)(uvw)(wv) =$

22) $2\left(e^{-i\omega t}xt\right)\left(te^{-i\omega t}x\right) =$

23) $3(m^3n^2)(mn)(2n^3) =$

24) $(x^2z)(z^3xy)(yx) =$

25) $(g^2l)(l^2g)(gl) =$

26) $-2(x^2z)(3yx)(4zxy) =$

27) $(2x^5)(3xy^2)(zx) =$

28) $(p^3qt)(2qp)(t^2q) =$

29) $7(m^4nq)(2mn)(qmn^2) =$

30) $(12pt)(3p)(t^2p) =$

31) $(pls)(2p^2s)(s^3pl) =$

32) $\left(\frac{z^5}{t}\right)\left(3\frac{z^5}{t}\right)(-2)\left(\frac{z^5}{t}\right) =$

33) $(33x^2)(xy)(zxy) =$

34) $\left(2\left(\frac{z}{t}\right)^3\right)\left(4\frac{z^5}{t}\right)\left(\frac{z^5}{t}\right)^6 =$

35) $\left(\frac{2x}{z}\right)^5\left(\frac{2x}{z}\right)\left(\frac{2x}{z}\right)^3 =$

36) $(\frac{m}{n^2})(2\left(\frac{m}{n^2}\right)^3) =$

37) $x^2(zy)(3y) =$

38) $4\left(\frac{x^2}{zy}\right)^2\left(4\left(\frac{x^2}{zy}\right)\right) =$

39) $(\frac{\sqrt{a^2+b^2}}{b})(3\left(\frac{\sqrt{a^2+b^2}}{b}\right)^3) =$

40) $\left(3\left(\frac{t^4}{g}\right)\right)\left(2\left(\frac{t^4}{g}\right)^{10}\right) =$

Multiplying and Dividing Monomials

✍ *Simplify.*

1) $\dfrac{3x^2yz^5}{xyz} =$

2) $\dfrac{25x(2xz^5)}{25x^2z^3} =$

3) $2\left(\dfrac{x^2m^5n^4}{x^3mn^4}\right)(2xn) =$

4) $3\dfrac{q}{r}\left(\dfrac{q^2r^5}{qr}\right) =$

5) $\dfrac{(3xy^3)(4xyz^3)}{12xyz} =$

6) $m^4(n^2)\left(\dfrac{5n^2}{m^3n^4}\right) =$

7) $\dfrac{3x(2xy)(3xz)}{9x^2} =$

8) $\left(\dfrac{3z^5x^2}{3z^3y}\right)\left(\dfrac{y}{z^3}\right) =$

9) $(3x^2y^2z^2)\left(\dfrac{2x}{x^2yz^2}\right) =$

10) $\left(\dfrac{e^{-i\omega t}}{t}\right)\left(\dfrac{t^3}{e^{-i\omega t}}\right) =$

11) $(3u^3v^2w)\left(\dfrac{1}{uvw^2}\right) =$

12) $2(mnl)(m^2nl^3)\left(\dfrac{1}{m^2l}\right) =$

13) $23(a^2b)\left(\dfrac{2ab}{b^2}\right) =$

14) $6(x^2zt)(xz^2t) =$

15) $\dfrac{3(ab)(c^2b)(abc)}{c^4a^3b} =$

16) $3x^2\left(\dfrac{(xz^3y)(2yz)}{x^2}\right)z^3 =$

17) $4x(12x^2)(z^4)\left(\dfrac{1}{z^3x^2}\right) =$

18) $\dfrac{(ab)(ab)^2(-2(ab)^5)}{(ab)^6} =$

19) $\left(\dfrac{x(w)^{2t}}{x(w)^t}\right)2xt =$

20) $2xt(t^5x)(2t^2) =$

21) $\left(\dfrac{(3a)(3b)(c^2ab)}{3(a^2bc^2)}\right) =$

22) $(-2x^2y)\left(\dfrac{1}{2zyx}\right) =$

23) $\dfrac{(x\sqrt{z})^5(2xz)(x\sqrt{z})}{2(x\sqrt{z})^3} =$

24) $3(x^2y^3)\left(\dfrac{2xy}{y^5zx^2}\right) =$

25) $(3uv^3)\left(\dfrac{uvw}{u^2vw}\right) =$

26) $(m^4n^6)(\dfrac{3nm(2n^2)}{3m^2n^3} =$

27) $x^2e^{3(i\omega t)}(\dfrac{15t}{e^{2(i\omega t)}x}) =$

28) $33xyz(2x^2zy) =$

29) $e^3hq\left(\dfrac{3hq}{6eq^2}\right) =$

30) $2(x^2z)(3zy)(zy) =$

31) $8z\left(\dfrac{2z^2-z^5}{8z^3}\right) =$

32) $\left(\dfrac{6q^4+3q^3}{3q}\right)\left(\dfrac{1}{q^2}\right) =$

33) $\left(\dfrac{1}{x^2-2x}\right)\left(\dfrac{10x^2-20x}{5}\right) =$

34) $(2x^2)\left(\dfrac{5}{x}\right) =$

GCF of Monomials

🖉 *Find the GCF of each set of monomials.*

1) $6x^2z, 2xy$

2) $2x^2y^5z, 14yz$

3) $3u^3vw^4, 6vw$

4) $10x^2yz, 5y^2x$

5) $3x^2z^4, \left(\frac{x^2z^2}{x^2z}\right)$

6) $9uv^5w, 3uw$

7) $4trq^5, \left(\frac{t^3rq}{trq}\right)$

8) $\left(\frac{12x^2z^4y}{x^2zy}\right), -2xzy$

9) $11n^4pm^5, 11pmn^2$

10) $14xz^4ty^5, \left(\frac{7x^2yt^3}{xt}\right)$

11) $6x^2y^3, xyz, 3x^2$

12) $15d^3eh^3, 5edh, 7deh^2$

13) $\left(\frac{2x^2y^5z}{yz}\right), 3xz, 4x^2y$

14) $33x^5zy^5, 22x^2y$

15) $\left(\frac{(-2xyz)(x^2)}{3x^3z}\right), 2xzy$

16) $21x^2mn, 35nx$

17) $3a(b^2ac), a^2c, 3ab$

18) $\left(\frac{m^4n^2p}{np}\right), 2m(nm)$

19) $15x^2\left(\frac{3x^2yz}{xz}\right), 5y^5zx^2$

20) $e^5hq, \left(\frac{3e^6h^4q}{e^4hq}\right)$

21) $\left(\frac{2x^2(4z^4x^2y)}{4xz^2y}\right), 32x^2yz$

22) $14mp^5t^4, 7m^6t^3p^2$

23) $\left(\frac{(-2mn)(n^4m^3)}{n^5m}\right), -n^5m^7$

24) $(x^2)(-7yz^5x^2), 2x^2y$

25) $25\left(\frac{x^2yz^4}{15yz}\right), 3x^2yz^8$

26) $(-3ab)(3bc), 3acb^2$

27) $\left(\frac{(ab)(bc)(ca)}{2ba^2}\right), 8a^3b^6c$

28) $9r^3q^5s^2, \left(\frac{(rsq^2)(3sq)}{3srq}\right)$

29) $2mny^3t, 4mty$

30) $3(abc)(2ca), 20a^2cb$

31) $2\frac{(x^2y^5z^4)}{2xz}, 2xy$

32) $3xy(2xyz), x^2z(yx)$

33) $25azx(3xz), 25a^3zx^2$

34) $33x^2+11x, 11x^2+22x$

35) $\frac{5}{(x-1)(x+3)}, \frac{-5}{x-1}$

36) $\frac{2x^5+x^2}{x}, x^2$

37) $2z^5+z, z^3$

38) $2x(1-y), (x-xy)$

Powers of monomials

✍ *Simplify.*

1) $\left(\frac{1}{2x}\right)\left(\frac{2x}{3}\right)^3 =$

2) $\left(\frac{3xy}{3z}\right)^2 (2z) =$

3) $\left(\frac{x^2zt}{2z^3}\right)^3 (8z^9) =$

4) $\left(\frac{(2x)^2}{yz}\right)^3 =$

5) $\left(\frac{(2m+1)}{3m^2}\right)^2 =$

6) $(zt^{10}b)^2(3z) =$

7) $(2x^2yz)^3 =$

8) $3(2mn^2)^4 =$

9) $(2x^2z^4y)^2 =$

10) $4(y^3xz)^5 =$

11) $(x^2y^2z^4)^3 =$

12) $(-2x^{ab}y^3)^3 =$

13) $\left(\frac{x^2y}{z}\right)^{ab} =$

14) $(-2a^6b^2c^4)^{5x} =$

15) $(x^2y^{2ab}z^{2b})^3 =$

16) $\left(\frac{x^2yz^5}{t}\right)^6 =$

17) $\left(\frac{(3x^2y^3z)}{2zy}\right)^2 =$

18) $(4x^2z^4)^{ab} =$

19) $(m^{10}n^6r)^3 =$

20) $(2yx^2z)^2 =$

21) $(x^2y^2z^3)^{2t} =$

22) $(3x^2yz^3)^5 =$

23) $\left(\frac{(2xyz^2)^4}{2xy}\right)^2 =$

24) $\left(\frac{(x^2yz^3)^3}{(xz)^2}\right)^2 =$

25) $\frac{(2xy)^3}{(x^2yz^4)^b} =$

26) $(x^2z)^2(2xy)^4 =$

27) $3(2x^2z)^5 =$

28) $(a^4bc^5)^{12} =$

29) $(10^x12^y5^z)^m =$

30) $(\propto^5 \beta^6 \gamma^8)^2 =$

31) $\left(\frac{(x^2y)^2(2zy)^2}{(xyz)^a}\right)^2 =$

32) $(2xy^5z^4x^2)^3 =$

33) $\left(\frac{x^2yz^2}{(xy)^a}\right)^b =$

34) $(t^6r^5s^6)^{(a+b)} =$

35) $2(x^2yx^4)^3 =$

36) $(abc^2)^2(a^2)^4 =$

37) $2(2x)^2(x^2yz)^2 =$

38) $(\frac{(xy^3z^2)^2}{x^2(2yz)^3}) =$

39) $(2x)^2(x^6z^3)^{\frac{1}{3}} =$

40) $(t^2x^2y^5)^{3ab} =$

Multiplying a Polynomial and a Monomial

✍️ *Find each product.*

1) $(2xy)\left(\frac{1}{2x+1}\right) =$

2) $\left(\frac{1}{3z+4}\right)\left(\frac{2xy+1}{3}\right) =$

3) $(-2rq)(3q - 3r + 1) =$

4) $\frac{3ca^3}{2}\left(1 + \frac{2}{ca}\right) =$

5) $3x(2x + 1) =$

6) $3b(b^2 - 1) =$

7) $2x(1 - 2x) =$

8) $\frac{x}{3}(3x^2 - 6y^3) =$

9) $yx^2(z^2 + xy) =$

10) $2x^4(z^2 - y) =$

11) $3ab(a^2 - b^2) =$

12) $z^2t\left(3ztx - \frac{2}{zt}\right) =$

13) $\frac{x}{y}\left(2x^2 + 3y - \frac{y}{x}\right) =$

14) $3ac(a^2 - 2ab + b^2) =$

15) $(-b)\left(\frac{3x}{2} + \frac{2x}{b}\right) =$

16) $a^b(x^2 - 2x + 4) =$

17) $(-2xy)(c - b + a) =$

18) $\rho\left(\frac{l}{s} - 2ls - s^2\right) =$

19) $2x^2yz(1 - 4x - 2y) =$

20) $y^3xz\left(25x - \frac{1}{y^3}\right) =$

21) $3uv(u^2 + 2uv + v^2) =$

22) $\left(-2\frac{x}{yz}\right)\left(\frac{2yz^2}{3x} - 2yz - xyz\right) =$

23) $3b^2(b^2 - 4ac) =$

24) $\frac{-b}{2a}(1 - b^2 - ac) =$

25) $5xy(3zx - xy + 2x^2) =$

26) $x^2y(3 - z) =$

27) $(2x + 2y - z)(-2y) =$

28) $2a(-x^2 - 2y^3 + xy) =$

29) $\frac{3xz}{y^3}\left(1 - \frac{2y^3}{xz}\right) =$

30) $7v(2ut - 2vt) =$

31) $4u^4(1 - 2v + 5w) =$

32) $\frac{x^2}{3z}\left(z^2 + 2z - \frac{2}{x^2}\right) =$

33) $6mz\left(\frac{12+m}{3z}\right) =$

34) $e^{2x}(1 - 3xz + 4y) =$

35) $\frac{2x^2}{z}(3 + 2z - y) =$

36) $(-x)^2(x^2 + 2x - 1) =$

37) $2v^2w\left(\frac{1-3u+5vw}{vw} - 1\right) =$

38) $2x^0(3x + 4z - 2zxy) =$

39) $4x(2x - 1) =$

40) $18x^2\left(\frac{1}{3x^2}\right) =$

Multiplying Binomials

✍ *Simplify each expression.*

1) $(x-5)(x+4) =$

2) $(x-6)(x-3) =$

3) $(x+4)(x+7) =$

4) $(x+3)(x-7) =$

5) $(3x-5)(2x+8) =$

6) $(11x-7)(5x+3) =$

7) $(4x-9)(9x+4) =$

8) $(x-2)(x+2) =$

9) $(x-2)(x-2) =$

10) $(x+4)(x-5) =$

11) $(3x-7)(x+3) =$

12) $(x-5)(4x+9) =$

13) $(3x+7)(8x-1) =$

14) $(x-1)(x+4) =$

15) $(10x+7)(x-11) =$

16) $(4x^2+1)(3-x) =$

✍ *Find the area of each shape.*

17)

x + 3

x + 3

19)

x + 6

x + 3

18)

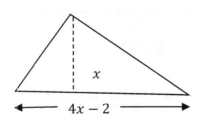

4x − 2

x

20)

2x + 7

x − 2

Factoring Trinomials

✎ *Factor each trinomial.*

1) $x^2 + 8x + 15 =$

2) $x^2 - 5x + 6 =$

3) $x^2 + 6x + 8 =$

4) $x^2 - 6x + 8 =$

5) $x^2 - 8x + 16 =$

6) $x^2 - 7x + 12 =$

7) $x^2 + 11x + 18 =$

8) $x^2 + 2x - 24 =$

9) $x^2 + 4x - 12 =$

10) $x^2 - 10x + 9 =$

11) $x^2 + 5x - 14 =$

12) $x^2 - 6x - 27 =$

13) $x^2 - 11x - 42 =$

14) $x^2 + 22x + 121 =$

15) $6x^2 + x - 12 =$

16) $x^2 - 17x + 30 =$

17) $3x^2 + 11x - 4 =$

18) $10x^2 + 33x - 7 =$

19) $x^2 + 24x + 144 =$

20) $8x^2 + 10x - 3 =$

✎ *Solve.*

21) A certain company's main source of income is a mobile app. The company's annual profit (in millions of dollars) as a function of the app's price (in dollars) is modeled by $P(x) = -2(x - 3)(x - 11)$. Which app prices will result in $0 annual profit?

22) A rectangular plot is 6 meters longer than it is wide. The area of the plot is 16 square meters. Find the length and width of the plot.

23) The combined area of two squares is 20 square centimeters. Each side of one square is twice as long as a side of the other square. Find the lengths of the sides of each square.

Answers of Worksheets

Writing Polynomials in Standard Form

1) $-4x^3 + 3x^2 + 1$

2) $-x^3 + 5x^2 + 7x$

3) $x^3 + 15$

4) $x^4 + 2x^2 + 2$

5) $x^2 - 1$

6) $-x^4 + 3x^2 + 7x$

7) $-4x^2 + 8x + 3$

8) $-x^3 + 3x - 6$

9) $10x^2 - 24x + 1$

10) $x^2 - 4x - 2$

11) $-5x^5 + 4x^3 + 2x$

12) $-2x^2 - 4x$

13) $x^2 + 5x + 1$

14) $-5x^3 + 4x + 4$

15) $-3y^2 + 16y$

16) $3m^4 + 4m^3 - 4m$

17) $-4x^2 - 8x$

18) $7x^3 + x + 1$

19) $2N^3 + N^2 + 2$

20) $x^{10} - 4x^5 + 17x^2$

21) $-3x^5 - 9x^2 + 4x$

22) $2x^2 + 3x + 3$

23) $-4x^3 + 5x^2 + 17x + 1$

24) $x^3 - 15x^2 - x + 9$

25) $14x^5 + \frac{1}{2}x^3 + \frac{1}{2}x^2$

26) $4x^3 + x^2 + 12x - 4$

27) $28x^5 + 4x^3 + 7x^2$

28) $34x^4 + 7x^2 - 2x$

29) $2x^4 + 8x^3 + x$

30) $-7x^3 - 3x^2 + 4x$

31) $5x^3 - \frac{25}{2}x^2$

32) $4x^5 + x^3 + x^2$

33) $-5x^2 - 4x$

34) $-4x^4 + 3x^2$

35) $6x^2 - 4x$

36) $x^5 + x^3 - x^2 + 5x$

37) $-x^2 + 2x + 4$

38) $z^3 + 2z - 3$

39) $p^6 + 3p^3 - 2$

40) $-2y^6 + y^4 + 2y$

41) $x^2 + 9x - 7$

42) $2x + 1$

43) $3z^3 + 5$

44) $q^2 - 3q + 2$

Simplifying Polynomials

1) $-20m^2 + 25m + 40$

2) $2d^6 - 14d^4 + 8d$

3) $28r^3s + 63rs^4 - 49r^2s^2$

4) $-64x^7 + 48x^5 + 56x^4$

5) $y^2 + 8y + 15$

6) $2x^2 + 22x + 36$

7) $16b^2 - 9$

8) $2n^2 - 12m^2 + 5mn$

9) $6x^3 + 26x^2 - 32$

10) $16z^2 + 48z + 36$

11) $-5x^2 + 19x - 18$

12) $16b^2 - 24b + 9$

13) $-24x^4 + 37x^3 - 41x^2 - 18x$

14) $14x^2 + 19x - 1$

15) $14x^3 + 42x^2$

16) $13x + 9y + 13$

17) $x^2 - 5xy - 9y^2$

Add and Subtract Monomials

1) $-9x^3y$

2) $(30uv - 5u)$

3) $7x^2z + z^2$

4) $3x^2y + x^2z$

5) $15x^2yz^2 - 2x$

6) $2\frac{x^2}{y}$

7) $2x^2 + \frac{1}{y}$

8) $5x^2z$

9) $5\frac{z}{y}x^2 + x^2$

10) $-12uvw$

11) $-2ux^2$

12) $4x^3 - xy$

13) $20y^2zx^2 + 17x^2$

14) $8m^6$

15) $14e^{-i\omega t}$

16) $11lq$

17) $2xyz$

18) $56\ lqr$

19) $14\frac{z^3x}{y}$

20) $8x^2z - 7y$

21) $3x^2zy$

22) $3x^2 - 12rs$

23) $-6z^3x$

24) $13x^2yx$

25) $-11xy$

26) $-4x^2y$

27) $11\frac{x^2}{z}$

28) $-8yzu$

29) $-35ut$

30) $18frq$

31) $24x - 21yz$

32) $10x^2 - 2y$

33) $7\frac{xyz}{t}$

34) $-7(t^2e^{-i\omega t})$

35) $5\frac{t^3x}{z} - x$

36) $-40wt$

37) $3x + 1$

38) $-x^3 - x$

39) $-z^2 - 4z$

40) $4x + 1$

41) $-3r^2 + r$

42) $3t^2$

Multiplying Monomials

1) $(2x)^4$

2) $2n^9$

3) $\frac{3x^{11}}{32}$

4) $\frac{16b^5}{27}$

5) $\frac{-1}{8x^7}$

6) $\frac{x^9}{64}$

7) $10x^2z^2$

8) $12x^3yz^2$

9) $12x^3yz$

10) $6x^3z^4y$

11) $7(x^3z^2t^3)$

12) $(-8u^3v^2w^2)$

13) $(-15)(m^4n^5)$

14) $2(x^3y^3z^2)$

15) $27v^7uw^6$

16) $6(x^7z^5y)$

17) $(3ac^4b^4)$

18) $84x^2yz^2$

19) $3x^4y^2z^4$

20) $-15xy^5z^6$

21) $3(u^5v^6w^2)$

22) $2(e^{-2i\omega t}x^2t)$

23) $6(m^4n^6)$

24) $(x^4z^4y^2)$

25) (g^4l^4)

26) $-24(x^4y^2z^2)$

27) $(6x^7y^2z)$

28) $(2p^4q^3t^3)$

29) $14(m^6n^4q^2)$

30) $(36p^3t^3)$

31) $2(p^4l^2s^5)$

32) $(-6)\frac{z^{15}}{t^3}$

33) $(33x^4y^2z)$

34) $8\frac{z^{38}}{t^{10}}$

35) $\frac{512x^9}{z^9}$

36) $2\left(\frac{m}{n^2}\right)^4$

37) $3x^2y^2z$

38) $16\left(\frac{x^2}{zy}\right)^3$

39) $3\left(\frac{\sqrt{a^2+b^2}}{b}\right)^4$

40) $6\left(\frac{t^4}{g}\right)^{11}$

Multiplying and Dividing Monomials

1) $3xz^4$

2) $2z^2$

3) $4m^4n$

4) $3q^2r^3$

5) xy^3z^2

6) $5m$

7) $2xyz$

8) $\frac{x^2}{z}$

9) $6xy$

10) t^2

11) $\left(\frac{3u^2v}{w}\right)$

12) $2(mn^2l^3)$

13) $46a^3$

14) $6(x^2z^3t^2)$

15) $\frac{3b^2}{ca}$

16) $6z^7xy^2$

17) $48xz$

18) $-2(ab)^2$

19) $2xwt$

20) $4x^2t^8$

21) $3b$

22) $\left(-\frac{x}{z}\right)$

23) $xz(x\sqrt{z})^3$

24) $\frac{6x}{yz}$

25) $3v^3$

26) $2m^3n^6$

27) $15txe^{(i\omega t)}$

28) $66x^3y^2z^2$

29) $\frac{1}{2}e^2h^2$

30) $6(x^2z^3y^2)$

31) $2-z^3$

32) $2q+1$

33) 2

34) $10x$

GCF of monomials

1) $2x$

2) $2yz$

3) $3vw$

4) $5xy$

5) z

6) $3uw$

7) t

8) $2z$

9) $11pmn^2$

10) $7xt$

11) x

12) deh

13) x

14) $11x^2y$

15) $2y$

16) xn

17) a

18) m^2n

19) $5x^2y$

20) e^2h

21) $2x^2z$

22) $7mp^2t^3$

23) $-m^3$

24) x^2y

25) x^2z^3

26) $3acb^2$

27) bc

28) q^2s

29) $2mty$

30) $2a^2cb$

31) $2xy$

32) x^2yz

33) $25azx^2$

34) $11x$

35) $\frac{5}{x-1}$

36) x

37) z

38) $x(1-y)$

Powers of monomials

1) $\frac{4x^2}{27}$

2) $\frac{2x^2y^2}{z}$

3) $x^6z^3t^3$

4) $\frac{64x^6}{y^3z^3}$

5) $\frac{(2m+1)^2}{9m^4}$

6) $3z^3t^{20}b^2$

7) $8x^6y^3z^3$

8) $48m^4n^8$

9) $4x^4z^8y^2$

10) $4y^{15}x^5z^5$

11) $x^6y^6z^{12}$

12) $-8x^{3ab}y^9$

13) $\frac{x^{2ab}y^{ab}}{z^{ab}}$

14) $(-2)^{5x}a^{30x}b^{10x}c^{20x}$

15) $x^6y^{6ab}z^{6b}$

16) $\frac{x^{12}y^6z^{30}}{t^6}$

17) $\frac{9x^4y^6z^2}{4z^2y^2}$

18) $4^{ab}x^{2ab}z^{4ab}$

19) $m^{30}n^{18}r^3$

20) $4y^2x^4z^2$

21) $x^{4t}y^{4t}z^{6t}$

22) $243x^{10}y^5z^{15}$

23) $\frac{256x^8y^8z^{16}}{4x^2y^2}$

24) $\frac{x^{12}y^6z^{18}}{x^4z^4}$

25) $\frac{8x^3y^3}{x^{2b}y^bz^{4b}}$

26) $16x^8z^2y^4$

27) $96x^{10}z^5$

28) $a^{48}b^{12}c^{60}$

29) $10^{mx}12^{my}5^{mz}$

30) $\propto^{10}\beta^{12}\gamma^{16}$

31) $\frac{16x^8y^8z^4}{x^{2a}y^{2a}z^{2a}}$

32) $8x^9y^{15}z^{12}$

33) $\frac{x^{2b}y^bz^{2b}}{x^{ab}y^{ab}}$

34) $t^{6(a+b)}r^{5(a+b)}s^{6(a+b)}$

35) $2x^6y^3x^{12}$

36) $a^{10}b^2c^4$

37) $8x^6y^2z^2$

38) $\frac{x^2y^6z^4}{8x^2y^3z^3}$

39) $4x^4z$

40) $t^{6ab}x^{6ab}y^{15ab}$

Multiplying a Polynomial and a Monomial

1) $\frac{2xy}{2x+1}$

2) $\frac{2xy+1}{9z+12}$

3) $-6rq^2 + 6r^2q - 2rq$

4) $\frac{3ca^3}{2} + 3a^2$

5) $6x^2 + 3x$

6) $3b^3 - 3b$

7) $2x - 4x^2$

8) $x^3 - 2xy^3$

9) $yx^2z^2 + x^3y^2$

10) $2x^4z^2 - 2x^4y$

11) $3a^3b - 3ab^3$

12) $3z^3t^2x - 2z$

13) $\frac{2x^3}{y} + 3x - 1$

14) $3ca^3 - 6a^2bc + 3acb^2$

15) $-\frac{3bx}{2} - 2x$

16) $x^2a^b - 2xa^b + 4a^b$

17) $-2xyc + 2xyb - 2xya$

18) $\frac{\rho l}{s} - 2\rho ls - \rho s^2$

19) $(2x^2yz - 82x^3yz - 4x^2y^2z)$

20) $25y^3x^2z - xz$

21) $3u^3v + 6u^2v^2 + 3uv^3$

22) $\frac{-4z}{3} + 4x + 2x^2$

23) $3b^4 - 12ab^2c$

24) $\frac{-b}{2a} + \frac{b^3}{2a} + \frac{bc}{2}$

25) $15x^2yz - 5x^2y^2 + 10x^3y$

26) $3x^2y - x^2yz$

27) $-4xy - 4y^2 + 2yz$

28) $-2ax^2 - 4ay^3 + 2axy$

29) $\frac{3xz}{y^3} - 6$

30) $14uvt - 14v^2t$

31) $u^4 - 8u^4v + 20u^4w$

32) $\frac{x^2z}{3} + \frac{2x^2}{3} - \frac{2}{3z}$

33) $24m + 2m^2$

34) $e^{2x} - 3xze^{2x} - 4ye^{2x}$

35) $\frac{6x^2}{z} + 4x^2 - \frac{2x^2y}{z}$

36) $x^4 + 2x^3 - x^2$

37) $2v - 6uv + 10v^2w - 2v^2w$

38) $(6x + 8z - 4zxy)$

39) $8x^2 - 4x$

40) 6

Multiplying Binomials

1) $x^2 - x - 20$

2) $x^2 - 9x + 18$

3) $x^2 + 11x + 28$

4) $x^2 - 4x - 21$

5) $6x^2 + 14x - 40$

6) $55x^2 - 2x - 21$

7) $36x^2 - 65x - 36$

8) $x^2 - 4$

9) $x^2 - 4x + 4$

10) $x^2 - x - 20$

11) $3x^2 + 2x - 21$

12) $4x^2 - 11x - 45$

13) $24x^2 + 53x - 7$

14) $x^2 + 3x - 4$

15) $10x^2 - 103x - 77$

16) $-4x^3 + 12x^2 - x + 3$

17) $x^2 + 6x + 9$

18) $x^2 - x$

19) $x^2 + 9x + 18$

20) $2x^2 + 3x - 14$

Factoring Trinomials

1) $(x + 3)(x + 5)$

2) $(x - 2)(x - 3)$

3) $(x + 4)(x + 2)$

4) $(x - 2)(x - 4)$

5) $(x - 4)(x - 4)$

6) $(x - 3)(x - 4)$

7) $(x + 2)(x + 9)$

8) $(x + 6)(x - 4)$

9) $(x - 2)(x + 6)$

10) $(x - 1)(x - 9)$

11) $(x - 2)(x + 7)$

12) $(x - 9)(x + 3)$

13) $(x + 3)(x - 14)$

14) $(x + 11)(x + 11)$

15) $(2x + 3)(3x - 4)$

16) $(x - 15)(x - 2)$

17) $(3x - 1)(x + 4)$

18) $(5x - 1)(2x + 7)$

19) $(x + 12)(x + 12)$

20) $(4x - 1)(2x + 3)$

21) $3, 11$

22) $w = 2, l = 8$

23) $s = 2$

Chapter 10:

Functions Operations

Topics that you'll practice in this chapter:

✓ Evaluating Function

✓ Adding and Subtracting Functions

✓ Multiplying and Dividing Functions

✓ Composition of Functions

Evaluating Function

✍ *Write each of following in function notation.*

1) $f = 10q - 2$

2) $g = -3s - 4$

3) $z = 1 - 6t$

4) $r = 9n + 12$

5) $d = 3m - 2$

6) $y = 3t^2 + t$

✍ *Evaluate each function.*

7) $f(x) = 3x^2 - 2x$, find $f(2)$

8) $h(x) = 6 - 4x$, find $h(-2)$

9) $w(x) = 3x - x^2$, find $f(-4)$

10) $f(x) = 7x - 12$, find $f(2)$

11) $g(a) = 6a + 2a^3$, find $f(-2)$

12) $y(r) = 33r - 27$, find $f(2)$

13) $g(t) = 30 - 6n$, find $f(5)$

14) $f(x) = -x^2 + 2x$, find $f(-2)$

15) $k(q) = 3q + 6$, find $f(3)$

16) $f(x) = x^2 - 2x + 1$, find $f(-2)$

17) $g(f) = 7f - f^3$, find $g(2)$

18) $f(g) = -2 + 5g$, find $f(-3)$

19) $f(r) = 13r + 10$, find $f(-1)$

20) $k(s) = 12s - 24$, find $k(3)$

21) $f(z) = 2z - z^2$, find $f(-3)$

22) $l(f) = 6f - 3$, find $l(-5)$

23) $p(q) = 3 - q^3$, find $p(2)$

24) $h(m) = 2m + 4$, find $h(-2)$

25) $g(t) = 3t^2 - 4t$, find $g(2)$

26) $k(b) = -15b + 24$, find $k(2x)$

27) $q(a) = a^2 + b$, find $k(b - 2)$

28) $h(u) = -4u + x$, find $h(2x)$

29) $h(x) = x^2 - \frac{x}{8}$, find $h(\frac{m}{2})$

30) $h(k) = 3k - 3x$, find $h(3x)$

Adding and Subtracting Functions

✎ *Perform the indicated operation.*

1) $f(x) = -3 + x$
   $g(x) = 2x - 3$
   Find $(f - 2g)(1)$

2) $g(t) = 4t + 1$
   $f(t) = 4t - 1$
   Find $(g - f)(-3)$

3) $l(s) = -2s + 4$
   $f(s) = 3s - 4$
   Find $(\frac{1}{2}l - f)(2)$

4) $g(m) = 12m - 8$
   $f(m) = 4 - 3m$
   Find $(g + f)(-1)$

5) $k(x) = 3 - 5x$
   $h(x) = x^2 + x$
   Find $k(2) - h(-2)$

6) $h(x) = 4x - x^2$
   $g(x) = x^2 - 1$
   Find $(h + 2g)(2)$

7) $l(r) = 6r + 7$
   $k(r) = 3 - 5r$
   Find $(l - k)(4)$

8) $h(n) = 6n + 2$
   $k(n) = -5n + 4$
   Find $(h - k)(2x)$

9) $g(x) = 3x^2 + 3$
   $f(x) = -x^2 + 4$
   Find $(g - f)(2)$

10) $g(k) = 3k + 1$
    $f(k) = 5 - 7k$
    Find $(g - f)(z)$

11) $l(a) = a^2 - 2a$
    $h(a) = 3a + 1$
    Find $(f + g)(x)$

12) $f(t) = 3t^2 - 1$
    $g(t) = 9 - 5t$
    Find $(f + g)(\frac{x}{2})$

Multiplying and Dividing Functions

✎ *Perform the indicated operation*.

1) $g(w) = 4w + 5$

   $f(w) = 6 - w$

   Find $(g.f)(-1)$

2) $f(m) = 2m^2$

   $h(m) = 1 - m$

   Find $(f.h)(-3)$

3) $k(b) = 3b + 1$

   $h(b) = b + 2$

   Find $(k.h)(-2)$

4) $t(x) = 2x - 3$

   $p(x) = 1 - 3x$

   Find $(\frac{t}{p})(-2)$

5) $f(y) = 3 - y$

   $g(y) = 2y + 1$

   Find $(\frac{f}{g})(-3)$

6) $g(c) = c^2 + 2c + 1$

   $f(c) = c + 1$

   Find $(\frac{g}{f})(5)$

7) $l(t) = 3t^2 - 3$

   $k(t) = \dfrac{1}{3t}$

   Find $(l.k)(-1)$

8) $g(v) = 2v - 2$

   $h(v) = v + 2$

   Find $(g.h)(1)$

9) $d(a) = a^2 - 2a$

   $b(a) = a$

   Find $(\frac{d}{b})(-2)$

10) $j(x) = 4x + 2$

    $f(x) = 3 - x$

    Find $(j.f)(-2)$

11) $l(s) = 3s + 1$

    $k(s) = -2s + 4$

    Find $(l.k)(x)$

12) $f(x) = 5x^2 - 6x$

    $g(x) = -x$

    Find $(\frac{f}{g})(2)$

Composition of Functions

✎ *Using* $f(x) = 3 - 4x$ *and* $g(x) = -7x$, *find*:

1) $f\big(g(-3)\big) =$

2) $f\big(g(-8)\big) =$

3) $g\big(f(6)\big) =$

4) $g\big(f(4)\big) =$

5) $f\big(g(7)\big) =$

6) $g\big(f(-5)\big) =$

✎ *Using* $f(x) = 5x^2 + 4$ *and* $g(x) = x - 1$, *find*:

7) $g\big(f(2)\big) =$

8) $g\left(f\left(\frac{4}{3}\right)\right) =$

9) $f\big(g(-5)\big) =$

10) $g\big(f(10)\big) =$

11) $g\big(f(2a)\big) =$

12) $g\big(f(b+1)\big) =$

✎ *Using* $f(a) = -2a + 3$ *and* $g(a) = 2 - 3a$, *find*:

13) $g\big(f(10)\big) =$

14) $f\big(f(3)\big) =$

15) $f\big(g(-2)\big) =$

16) $f\big(f(2m)\big) =$

17) $g\big(f(-x)\big) =$

18) $g\big(g(2+x)\big) =$

✎ *Using* $f(x) = -4x$ *and* $g(x) = 5x - 8$, *find*:

19) $f\big(g(9)\big) =$

20) $g\big(f(-8)\big) =$

21) $f\big(g(14)\big) =$

22) $f\big(f(-5)\big) =$

23) $g\big(f(6)\big) =$

24) $g\big(g(0)\big) =$

Answers of Worksheets

Evaluating Function

1) $f(q) = 10q - 2$
2) $g(s) = -3s - 4$
3) $z(t) = 1 - 6t$
4) $r(n) = 9n + 12$
5) $d(m) = 3m - 2$
6) $y(t) = 3t^2 + t$
7) 8
8) 14
9) -28
10) 2
11) -28
12) 39
13) 0
14) -8
15) 15

16) 9
17) 6
18) -17
19) -3
20) 12
21) -15
22) -33
23) -5
24) 0
25) 4
26) $-30x + 24$
27) $b^2 - 3b + 4$
28) $-7x$
29) $\frac{m}{4}\left(m - \frac{1}{4}\right)$
30) $6x$

Adding and Subtracting Functions

1) 0
2) 2
3) -2
4) -13
5) -9
6) 10

7) 48
8) $22x - 2$
9) 15
10) $10z - 4$
11) $x^2 + x + 1$
12) $\frac{3}{4}x^2 - \frac{5}{2}x + 8$

Multiplying and Dividing Functions

1) 7

2) 72

3) 0

4) --1

5) $--\frac{6}{5}$

6) 6

7) 0

8) 0

9) -4

10) -30

11) $-6x^2 + 10x + 4$

12) -4

Composition of Functions

1) --81

2) --221

3) 147

4) 91

5) 199

6) --161

7) 23

8) $\frac{107}{9}$

9) 184

10) 503

11) $20a^2 + 3$

12) $5b^2 + 10b + 8$

13) 53

14) 9

15) -13

16) $8m - 3$

17) $-6x - 7$

18) $9x + 14$

19) -148

20) 152

21) -248

22) -80

23) -128

24) -48

Chapter 11:

Quadratic

Topics that you'll practice in this chapter:

- ✓ Solving Quadratic Equations

- ✓ Use the Quadratic Formula and the Discriminant

- ✓ Solve Quadratic Inequalities

- ✓ Graphing Quadratic Functions

Solving Quadratic Equations

✎ *Solve each equation by factoring or using the quadratic formula.*

1) $(2x - 2)(x + 7) = 0$

2) $(3x + 3)(2x + 5) = 0$

3) $(6x + 9)(4x + 4) = 0$

4) $(x + 8)(x - 8) = 0$

5) $(3x + 9)(2x + 6) = 0$

6) $(7x + 14)(3x - 5) = 0$

7) $(-2x - 6)(2x - 8) = 0$

8) $(3 - 6x)(2x + 9) = 0$

9) $(12x - 9)(3x - 9) = 0$

10) $(-2x + 1)(3 - 6x) = 0$

11) $4x^2 = -2x - x^2$

12) $2x^2 - 12 = 2x$

13) $3x^2 - 12 = 5x$

14) $-x^2 + 8 = 2x$

15) $x^2 + 5x = 24$

16) $x^2 - 3x = 18$

17) $x^2 - 6x = 55$

18) $x^2 + 7x = 8$

19) $x^2 - 6x = 16$

20) $x^2 - 3x - 24 = 2x$

21) $x^2 - 13x = 30$

22) $2x^2 - 4x = 30$

23) $3x^2 = 3x - 60$

24) $3x^2 - 6x - 72 = 0$

25) $x^2 - 21 = 4x$

26) $2x^2 - 4x = 6$

27) $-6x^2 + 30 = 24x$

28) $x^2 + 12x = 45$

29) $-8x^2 - 14x + 18 = 3$

30) $2x^2 - 8 = 0$

31) $3x^2 + 10x + 3 = 0$

32) $2x^2 - x - 15 = x^2 + 5$

Quadratic Formula and the Discriminant

✎ *Find the value of the discriminant of each quadratic equation.*

1) $x^2 - 5x + 6 = 0$

2) $2x^2 - 4x + 6 = 0$

3) $3x^2 - 5x + 4 = 0$

4) $4x^2 - x + 10 = 0$

5) $2x^2 + x + 1 = 0$

6) $x^2 + 2x - 1 = 0$

7) $10x^2 + 5x - 4 = 0$

8) $5x^2 + 12x + 2 = 0$

9) $4x^2 - 6x + 2 = 0$

10) $-3x^2 + 5x - 8 = 0$

11) $-2x^2 - 8x + 12 = 0$

12) $-2x^2 + 2 = 0$

13) $9x^2 + 2x - 6 = 0$

14) $-4x^2 - 2x + 4 = 0$

15) $-6x^2 + 4x + 4 = 0$

16) $-3x^2 + x + 6 = 0$

17) $5x^2 - 2x - 8 = 0$

18) $2x^2 - 2x + 6 = 0$

19) $8x^2 - 8x - 2 = 0$

20) $-6x^2 - x + 5 = 0$

✎ *Find the discriminant of each quadratic equation then state the number of real and imaginary solutions.*

21) $-3x^2 + 5 = -2x$

22) $x^2 = -2x + 5$

23) $4x^2 - 5x = -8$

24) $7x^2 + 2x - 4 = 3x^2$

25) $-3x^2 = +4x - 2$

26) $8x^2 + 2x - 6 = 4$

27) $3x^2 + 6x + 2 = 0$

28) $-4x^2 + 2x - 7 = 0$

Quadratic Inequalities

✍ *Solve each quadratic inequality.*

1) $-4x^2 > 8x - 32$

2) $x^2 - 3x < 4$

3) $3x^2 + 2x - 5 > 3$

4) $2x^2 > 2x + 4$

5) $4x^2 < -4x$

6) $-4x^2 + 8 < 4x - 16$

7) $-2x^2 + 8 < 4x^2 - 2x$

8) $-3x > -5x^2 - 2$

9) $-3x > 5x^2 - 2$

10) $10x^2 + 5x > -5x^2 + 10$

11) $5x - x^2 > 2x$

12) $-2x^2 - 4 < -4x - 2$

13) $-4x^2 + 4x < -4x^2 - 16$

14) $-6x + 4 < 3x^2 - 5$

15) $x^2 > -3x^2 + 12x$

16) $4x^2 + 2x - 8 \le 4$

17) $-3x^2 + 6x + 3 \ge 3$

18) $8x^2 + 12x < 36$

19) $4x^2 + 5x < -6x^2 + 10x + 5$

20) $-3x^2 - 9 > 3x - 15$

21) $-12x^2 - 4x > 32x + 24$

22) $-25x^2 + 4 < -13x^2 - 8$

23) $-5x^2 + 6x > x^2 - 12$

24) $15x^2 + 12x > -25x^2$

25) $-8x^2 - 4x < 12x - 24$

26) $14 - 7x^2 > 21x + 28$

27) $-5x - 30x^2 < -35x^2 + 10$

28) $-x^2 + 2x > -3x + 4$

29) $5x^2 + 9x < -13x^2 + 27$

30) $-11x^2 + 2x < -9x - 330$

31) $-5x^2 + 4 > -3x^2 + 2x$

32) $-3x^2 + 12x - 9 > 0$

Graphing Quadratic Functions

✎ *Sketch the graph of each function. Identify the vertex and axis of symmetry.*

1) $y = (x - 2)^2 - 3x$

2) $y = -(2x + 4)^2 - x$

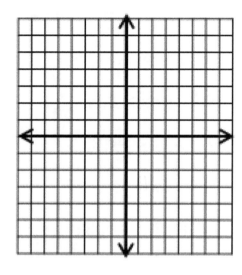
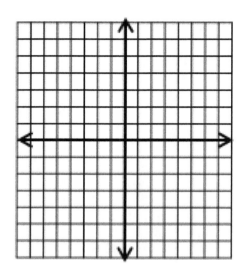

3) $y = 2x^2 - 3x + 1$

4) $y = \dfrac{x^2 - 4x}{4}$

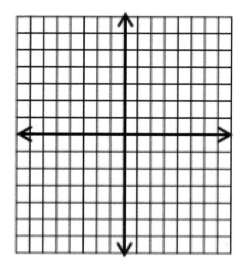
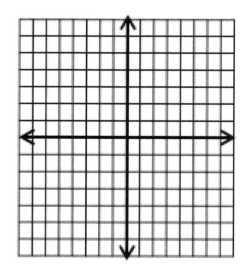

Answers of Worksheets

Solving quadratic equations

1) $\{1, -7\}$
2) $\{-1, -\frac{5}{2}\}$
3) $\{-\frac{3}{2}, -1\}$
4) $\{-8, 8\}$
5) -3
6) $\{-2, -\frac{5}{3}\}$
7) $\{-3, 4\}$
8) $\{\frac{1}{2}, -\frac{9}{2}\}$
9) $\{\frac{3}{4}, 3\}$
10) $\frac{1}{2}$

11) $\{0, -\frac{2}{5}\}$
12) $\{3, -2\}$
13) $\{3, -\frac{4}{3}\}$
14) $\{-4, 2\}$
15) $\{3, -8\}$
16) $\{6, -3\}$
17) $\{11, -5\}$
18) $\{1, -8\}$
19) $\{-2, 8\}$
20) $\{8, -3\}$
21) $\{15, -2\}$
22) $\{5, -3\}$

23) $\{5, -4\}$
24) $\{6, -4\}$
25) $\{-3, 7\}$
26) $\{3, -1\}$
27) $\{1, -5\}$
28) $\{-15, 3\}$
29) $\{-\frac{5}{2}, \frac{3}{4}\}$
30) $\{-2, 2\}$
31) $\{-3, -\frac{1}{3}\}$
32) $\{5, -4\}$

Quadratic formula and the discriminant

1) 1
2) -32
3) -23
4) -159
5) -7
6) 4
7) 185
8) 104
9) 4
10) 121
11) 160
12) 16
13) 220
14) 68

15) 112
16) 73
17) 164
18) -44
19) 128
20) 121
21) $64, two\ real\ solution$
22) $24, two\ real\ solution$
23) $-103, two\ imaginary\ solution$
24) $68, two\ real\ solution$
25) $40, two\ real\ solution$
26) $324, two\ real\ solution$
27) $12, two\ real\ solution$
28) $-108,\ two\ imaginary\ solution$

Solve quadratic inequalities

1) $-4 < x < 2$
2) $-1 < x < 4$
3) $x < -2 \ or \ x > \frac{4}{3}$
4) $x < -1 \ or \ x > 2$
5) $-1 < x < 0$
6) $x < -3 \ or \ x > 2$
7) $x \leq -1 \ or \ x \geq \frac{4}{3}$

8) $all\ real\ numbers$
9) $-1 < x < \frac{2}{5}$
10) $x < -1 \ or \ x > \frac{2}{3}$
11) $0 < x < 3$
12) $x < 1 \ or \ x > 1$
13) $x < -4$
14) $x < -3 \ or \ x > 1$

15) $x < 0 \ or \ x > 3$
16) $-2 \leq x \leq \frac{3}{2}$
17) $0 \leq x \leq 2$
18) $-3 < x < \frac{3}{2}$
19) $-\frac{1}{2} < x < 1$
20) $-2 < x < 1$
21) $-2 < x < -1$

22) $x < -1 \; or \; x > 1$

23) $-1 < x < 2$

24) $x < -\frac{3}{10} \; or \; x > 0$

25) $x < -3 \; or \; x > 1$

26) $-2 < x < -1$

27) $-1 < x < 2$

28) $1 < x < 4$

29) $-\frac{3}{2} < x < 1$

30) $x < -5 \; or \; x > 6$

31) $-2 < x < 1$

32) $1 < x < 3$

Graphing quadratic functions

1) $(2, -6), x = 2$

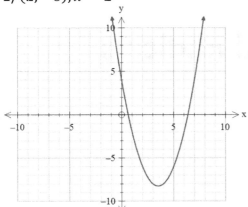

2) $(-2, +2), x = -2$

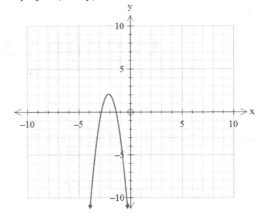

3) $(0, 1), x = 0$

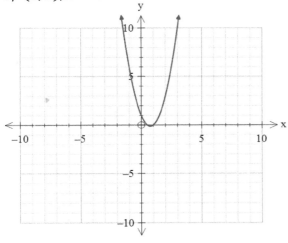

4) $(1, -\frac{3}{4}), x = 1$

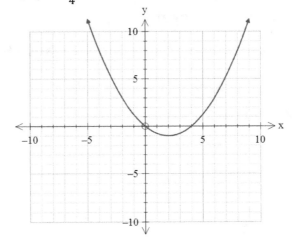

Chapter 12:

Exponents and Radicals

Topics that you'll learn in this part:

✓ Multiplication Property of Exponents

✓ Division Property of Exponents

✓ Powers of Products and Quotients

✓ Zero and Negative Exponents

✓ Negative Exponents and Negative Bases

✓ Writing Scientific Notation

✓ Square Roots

Multiplication Property of Exponents

✍ *Simplify*

1) $4x^4 \times 4x^4 \times 4x^4 =$

2) $2x^2 \times x^2 =$

3) $x^4 \times 3x =$

4) $x \times 2x^2 =$

5) $5x^4 \times 5x^4 =$

6) $2yx^2 \times 2x =$

7) $3x^4 \times y^2x^4 =$

8) $y^2x^3 \times y^5x^2 =$

9) $4yx^3 \times 2x^2y^3 =$

10) $6x^2 \times 6x^3y^4 =$

11) $3x^4y^5 \times 7x^2y^3 =$

12) $7x^2y^5 \times 9xy^3 =$

13) $7xy^4 \times 4x^3y^3 =$

14) $3x^5y^3 \times 8x^2y^3 =$

15) $3x \times y^5x^3 \times y^4 =$

16) $yx^2 \times 2y^2x^2 \times 2xy =$

✍ *Solve.*

17) There are 7^6 pieces of leaves on a tree, and there are 7^4 trees in a forest. How many pieces of leaves are there in the forest?

18) In a storage warehouse, each container weights 6^3 pounds. If there are 6^5 containers, how much do the crates weigh in total?

19) You own a microscope with an objective lens and an eyepiece. The objective lens can magnify an object 10^3 times, and the eyepiece can further magnify an object 10^2 times. What is the maximum magnification on your microscope?

20) An asteroid travel at a speed of 8^8 miles per day, how many miles will it travel in 8^3 day?

Division Property of Exponents

✎ *Simplify*

1) $\dfrac{3x^3}{2x^5}$

2) $\dfrac{12x^3}{14x^6}$

3) $\dfrac{12x^3}{9y^8}$

4) $\dfrac{25xy^4}{5x^6y^2}$

5) $\dfrac{2x^4}{7x}$

6) $\dfrac{16x^2y^8}{4x^3}$

7) $\dfrac{12x^4}{15x^7y^9}$

8) $\dfrac{12yx^4}{10yx^8}$

9) $\dfrac{16x^4y}{9x^8y^2}$

✎ *Solve.*

10) Dalloway's room has the dimensions $3a^7$ by, $4b^3$ by, $5b^2$. What is the volume of Dalloway's room?

11) The fuel tank of Mr. Lee's car has the dimensions b^5 by $3c^2$ by $2c^3$. What is the volume of the fuel tank?

12) A factory produces wardrobes and likes to use exponents as dimensions. The wardrobes have the dimensions b^4 by b^4 by $5c^6$. What is the volume of the wardrobes?

13) The annual corn yield is $5a^2 kg$ per hectare. If there are $2b^8$ hectares of corn field in Nebraska and $7b^7$ hectares of corn field in Illinois, what is the total annual corn yield in these two states?

14) The dimensions of a water tank are a^2mm by a^5mm by $3b^2$mm. If 1ml water may contain $3c^{21}$ water molecules, how many water molecules are there in the water tank?

Powers of Products and Quotients

📖*Simplify.*

1) $(2yx^2)^3 =$

2) $(2z^3y^3x)^4 =$

3) $\left(\frac{x^2yz}{4}\right)^3 =$

4) $(a^{10}b^3c)^2 =$

5) $(2x^2zy^5)^3 =$

6) $\left(\frac{2x}{z^2}y^4\right)^5 =$

7) $(2r^5q^2t^2)^3 =$

8) $\left(\frac{3x^2yz^4}{2m^4n}\right)^3 =$

9) $(10^2.10^3)^8 =$

10) $(3^a.3^b)^4 =$

11) $\left(2x^3y^{10}\frac{z}{3}\right)^3 =$

12) $(xz^4y^{10})^5 =$

13) $(\frac{m^6n^4t^3}{2x^2})^5 =$

14) $\left(\frac{i^3j^5k^3}{2ik}\right)^5 =$

15) $(6^5.6^2.6^0)^2 =$

16) $(e^2.e^4)^4 =$

17) $\left(t^2\frac{p^2}{q^4}\right)^6 =$

18) $\left(y^5x^4\frac{1}{z^6}\right)^3 =$

19) $\left(\frac{2x.3y}{3z.x^2}\right)^3 =$

20) $(3xy.4xy)^3 =$

21) $(-j^3.2j)^3 =$

22) $(\frac{-2x^2y^2}{z})^3 =$

23) $(-3e^{2t}e^{2\omega t})^3 =$

24) $\left(\frac{25x^{10}y^8}{3z^9}\right)^0 =$

25) $\left(\frac{(-2x)^2}{(-2yz)^3}\right)^3 =$

26) $(4x^2y^4)^4 =$

27) $(2x^4y^4)^3 =$

28) $(3x^2y^2)^2 =$

29) $(3x^4y^3)^4 =$

30) $(2x^6y^8)^2 =$

31) $(12x^3x)^3 =$

32) $(2x^9x^6)^3 =$

33) $(5x^{10}y^3)^3 =$

34) $(4x^3x^3)^2 =$

35) $(3x^3.5x)^2 =$

36) $(10x^{11}y^3)^2 =$

37) $(9x^7y^5)^2 =$

38) $(4x^4y^6)^5 =$

39) $(3x.4y^3)^2 =$

40) $(\frac{5x}{x^2})^2 =$

41) $\left(\frac{x^4y^4}{x^2y^2}\right)^3 =$

42) $\left(\frac{25x}{5x^6}\right)^2 =$

43) $\left(\frac{x^8}{x^6y^2}\right)^2 =$

44) $\left(\frac{xy^2}{x^3y^3}\right)^{-2} =$

45) $\left(\frac{2xy^4}{x^3}\right)^2 =$

46) $\left(\frac{xy^4}{5xy^2}\right)^{-3} =$

47) $((3xyz)^2)^{\frac{1}{2}} =$

48) $(x^2y^2)^{\frac{1}{2}} =$

49) $3x(w^3)^3 =$

50) $\left(\frac{2x}{(2-x)}\right)^2 =$

51) $\left(\frac{2}{3x^2y}\right)^3(y^2x) =$

52) $\frac{(2rq^2)^2}{(-q)^3} =$

53) $\left(\frac{-x^4}{3zy}\right)^2 =$

54) $(2x.x.x^2)^3 =$

55) $(-xy)^2 =$

56) $\frac{(2x^2y)^4}{4x^3} =$

57) $(3x^2)^{t+1} =$

58) $\left(\frac{2tx^2}{3xt^3}\right)^m =$

59) $(3xyz^5)^r =$

Zero and Negative Exponents

✍️ *Evaluate the following expressions.*

1) $8^{-1} =$

2) $8^{-2} =$

3) $2^{-4} =$

4) $10^{-2} =$

5) $9^{-1} =$

6) $3^{-2} =$

7) $7^{-2} =$

8) $3^{-4} =$

9) $6^{-2} =$

10) $5^{-3} =$

11) $22^{-1} =$

12) $4^{-2} =$

13) $5^{-2} =$

14) $35^{-1} =$

15) $4^{-3} =$

16) $6^{-3} =$

17) $3^{-5} =$

18) $5^{-2} =$

19) $2^{-3} =$

20) $3^{-3} =$

21) $7^{-3} =$

22) $6^{-3} =$

23) $8^{-3} =$

24) $9^{-2} =$

25) $10^{-3} =$

26) $10^{-9} =$

27) $(\frac{1}{2})^{-1} =$

28) $(\frac{1}{2})^{-2} =$

29) $(\frac{1}{3})^{-2} =$

30) $(\frac{2}{3})^{-2} =$

31) $(\frac{1}{5})^{-3} =$

32) $(\frac{3}{4})^{-2} =$

33) $(\frac{2}{5})^{-2} =$

34) $(\frac{1}{2})^{-8} =$

35) $(\frac{2}{5})^{-3} =$

36) $(\frac{3}{7})^{-2} =$

37) $(\frac{5}{6})^{-3} =$

38) $\left(\frac{x^2}{e^{-2t}}\right)^{-2} =$

39) $(3xz^{-3})^2 =$

40) $\left(\frac{(a^3)^{-2}}{b}\right)^{-2} =$

41) $\left(\frac{x^2 y}{(-2z)^2}\right)^{-3} =$

42) $\left(\frac{gh^3}{2k}\right)^{-3} =$

43) $\left(\frac{2sqr^2}{2x}\right)^{-1} =$

44) $\left(\frac{25xyz}{33mn^3}\right)^0 =$

45) $(2xy(x^2)^{-2})^{-1} =$

46) $(x^2 z^3)^{-3} =$

47) $\left(\frac{1}{3}xy^2\right)^{-2} =$

48) $\frac{(y^{20} x^{15})^0}{(2x)^{-2}} =$

49) $(-3xy)^{-2} =$

50) $(e^{-\omega t})(e^{\omega t}) =$

51) $(3x + y)^{-2} =$

52) $\frac{(4x+1)^{-1}}{(9x)^{-3}} =$

53) $\left(\frac{2y}{zx}\right)^{-3} =$

54) $\left(\frac{1}{2}\right)^{-5} =$

55) $\left(\frac{3}{(2-2x^2)}\right)^{-2} =$

56) $(\frac{1}{2x+1})^{-1}(2x + 1)^{-1} =$

57) $(1 - x)^{-2} =$

58) $(x^2)^{-2} =$

59) $(x^{-2}zy)^{-2} =$

60) $(x^{-1}z)^2 =$

61) $(yz^{-2})^{-1} =$

62) $(2x)^{-3}(x^2) =$

Writing Scientific Notation

✎ *Write each number in scientific notation.*

1) $0.113 =$

2) $0.02 =$

3) $2.5 =$

4) $20 =$

5) $60 =$

6) $0.004 =$

7) $78 =$

8) $1,600 =$

9) $1,450 =$

10) $91,000 =$

11) $2,000,000 =$

12) $0.0000006 =$

13) $354,000 =$

14) $0.000325 =$

15) $0.00023 =$

16) $56,000,000 =$

17) $21,000 =$

18) $78,000,000 =$

19) $0.0000022 =$

20) $0.00012 =$

21) $0.02 =$

✎ *Solve.*

22) A color photograph taken with a digital camera is converted into digital format using 4×10^0 bytes per pixel. Photographs taken with the camera each have 2.2×10^6 pixels. How many bytes are there in one photo? Write your answer in scientific notation.

23) A certain animated movie earned 1.1×10^9 in revenues at the box office. The movie lasts $\$9.1 \times 10^1$ minute. How much revenue was earned per minute of the movie? Write your final answer in scientific notation

24) The weight of a honeybee is $1.2 \times 10^{-1} g$,. The weight of the pollen collected by the bee on one trip is $6.2 \times 10^{-2} g$. What is the combined weight of the bee and the pollen? Express your answer in scientific notation.

Square Roots

✏️ *Find the value each square root.*

1) $\sqrt{1} =$	8) $\sqrt{0} =$	15) $\sqrt{256} =$
2) $\sqrt{4} =$	9) $\sqrt{64} =$	16) $\sqrt{289} =$
3) $\sqrt{9} =$	10) $\sqrt{81} =$	17) $\sqrt{324} =$
4) $\sqrt{25} =$	11) $\sqrt{121} =$	18) $\sqrt{400} =$
5) $\sqrt{16} =$	12) $\sqrt{225} =$	19) $\sqrt{900} =$
6) $\sqrt{49} =$	13) $\sqrt{144} =$	20) $\sqrt{529} =$
7) $\sqrt{36} =$	14) $\sqrt{100} =$	21) $\sqrt{90} =$

✏️ *Evaluate.*

22) $8\sqrt{2} \times 2\sqrt{2} =$	29) $\sqrt{81} - \sqrt{3} =$	35) $\sqrt{36} - 5\sqrt{6} =$
23) $6\sqrt{3} - \sqrt{12} =$	30) $\sqrt{144} + \sqrt{12} =$	36) $\sqrt{121} -$
24) $3\sqrt{3} + \sqrt{27} =$	31) $\sqrt{289} - \sqrt{17} =$	$\quad 2\sqrt{11} =$
25) $\sqrt{8} - \sqrt{2} =$	32) $3\sqrt{18} - 3\sqrt{2} =$	37) $\sqrt{10} \times \sqrt{6} =$
26) $\sqrt{27} \times \sqrt{3} =$	33) $\frac{3\sqrt{3}}{\sqrt{3}} =$	38) $\sqrt{3} \times \sqrt{5} =$
27) $4\sqrt{5} + \sqrt{25} =$		39) $\sqrt{11} \times \sqrt{3} =$
28) $\sqrt{169} - \sqrt{13} =$	34) $\frac{\sqrt{4} \times \sqrt{2}}{3\sqrt{2}} =$	40) $\sqrt{7} + \sqrt{28} =$

✏️ *Solve.*

41) Which of the following is equal to the square root of 75?

A. $2\sqrt{6}$ 	 C. $5\sqrt{3}$

B. $36\sqrt{2}$ 	 D. $12\sqrt{6}$

Answers of Worksheets

Multiplication Property of Exponents

1) $64x^{12}$
2) $2x^4$
3) $3x^5$
4) $2x^3$
5) $25x^8$

6) $4x^3y$
7) $3x^8y^2$
8) x^5y^7
9) $8x^5y^4$
10) $36x^5y^4$

11) $21x^6y^8$
12) $63x^3y^8$
13) $28x^4y^7$
14) $24x^7y^6$
15) $3x^4y^9$

16) $4x^5y^4$
17) 7^{10}
18) 6^8
19) 10^5
20) 8^{11}

Division Property of Exponents

1) $\frac{3}{2x^2}$
2) $\frac{6}{7x^3}$
3) $\frac{4x^3}{3y^8}$
4) $\frac{5y^2}{x^5}$

5) $\frac{2x^3}{7}$
6) $\frac{4y^8}{x}$
7) $\frac{4}{5x^3y^9}$
8) $\frac{6}{5x^4}$

9) $\frac{16}{9x^4y}$
10) $60a^7b^5$
11) $6b^5c^5$
12) $5b^8c^6$
13) $10a^2b^8 +$

$35a^2b^7$
14) $9a^7b^2c^{21}$
15) $4b^6c^3$

Powers of Products and Quotients

1) $8y^3x^6$
2) $16z^{12}y^{12}x^4$
3) $\frac{x^6y^3z^3}{64}$
4) $a^{20}b^6c^2$
5) $8x^6z^3y^{15}$
6) $\frac{32x^5}{z^{10}}y^{20}$
7) $8r^{15}q^6t^6$
8) $\frac{27x^6y^3z^{12}}{8m^{12}n^3}$
9) 10^{40}
10) $3^{4(a+b)}$
11) $8x^9y^{30}\frac{z^3}{27}$

12) $x^5z^{20}y^{50}$
13) $\frac{m^{30}n^{20}t^{15}}{32x^{10}}$
14) $\frac{i^{10}j^{15}k^{10}}{32}$
15) 6^{14}
16) e^{24}
17) $t^{12}\frac{p^{12}}{q^{24}}$
18) $y^{15}x^{12}\frac{1}{z^{18}}$
19) $\frac{8y^3}{z^3.x^3}$
20) $1728x^6y^6$
21) $-8j^{12}$
22) $\frac{-8x^6y^6}{z^3}$

23) $-27e^{6t(1+\omega)}$
24) 1
25) $\frac{x^6}{-8y^9z^9}$
26) $256x^8y^{16}$
27) $8x^{12}y^{12}$
28) $9x^4y^4$
29) $81x^{16}y^{12}$
30) $4x^{12}y^{16}$
31) $1,728x^{12}$
32) $8x^{45}$
33) $125x^{30}y^9$
34) $16x^{12}$

35) $225x^8$
36) $100x^{22}y^6$
37) $81x^{14}y^{10}$
38) $1,024x^{20}y^{30}$
39) $144x^2y^6$
40) $\frac{25}{x^2}$
41) x^6y^6
42) $\frac{25}{x^{10}}$
43) $\frac{x^4}{y^4}$
44) x^4y^2
45) $\frac{4y^8}{x^4}$

46) $\frac{125}{y^6}$

47) $3xyz$

48) xy

49) $3xw^6$

50) $\frac{4x^2}{(2-x)^2}$

51) $\frac{8}{27x^5y}$

52) $-2r^2q$

53) $\frac{x^8}{9z^2y^2}$

54) $8x^{12}$

55) x^2y^2

56) $4x^5y^4$

57) $3^{t+1}x^{2t+2}$

58) $\frac{2^m x^m}{3^m t^{2m}}$

59) $3^r x^r y^r z^{5r}$

Zero and Negative Exponents

1) $\frac{1}{8}$

2) $\frac{1}{64}$

3) $\frac{1}{16}$

4) $\frac{1}{100}$

5) $\frac{1}{9}$

6) $\frac{1}{9}$

7) $\frac{1}{49}$

8) $\frac{1}{81}$

9) $\frac{1}{36}$

10) $\frac{1}{125}$

11) $\frac{1}{22}$

12) $\frac{1}{16}$

13) $\frac{1}{25}$

14) $\frac{1}{35}$

15) $\frac{1}{64}$

16) $\frac{1}{216}$

17) $\frac{1}{243}$

18) $\frac{1}{25}$

19) $\frac{1}{8}$

20) $\frac{1}{27}$

21) $\frac{1}{343}$

22) $\frac{1}{216}$

23) $\frac{1}{512}$

24) $\frac{1}{81}$

25) $\frac{1}{1,000}$

26) $\frac{1}{1,000,000,000}$

27) 2

28) 4

29) 9

30) $\frac{9}{4}$

31) 125

32) $\frac{16}{9}$

33) $\frac{25}{4}$

34) 256

35) $\frac{125}{8}$

36) $\frac{49}{9}$

37) $\frac{216}{125}$

38) $\frac{1}{e^{4t}x^2}$

39) $\frac{9x^2}{z^6}$

40) $a^{12}b^2$

41) $\frac{64z^6}{x^6y^3}$

42) $\frac{8k^3}{g^3h^9}$

43) $\frac{x}{sqr^2}$

44) 1

45) $\frac{x^3}{2y}$

46) $\frac{1}{x^6z^9}$

47) $\frac{9}{x^2y^4}$

48) $4x^2$

49) $\frac{1}{9x^2y^2}$

50) 1

51) $\frac{1}{(3x+y)^2}$

52) $\frac{729x^3}{4x+1}$

53) $\frac{z^3x^3}{8y^3}$

54) 32

55) $\frac{(2-2x^2)^2}{9}$

56) 1

57) $\frac{1}{(1-x)^2}$

58) $\frac{1}{x^4}$

59) $\frac{x^4}{z^2y^2}$

60) $\frac{z^2}{x^2}$

61) $\frac{z^2}{y}$

62) $\frac{1}{8x}$

Writing Scientific Notation

1) 1.13×10^{-1}

2) 2×10^{-2}

3) 2.5×10^0

4) 2×10^1

5) 6×10^1

6) 4×10^{-3}

7) 7.8×10^1

8) 1.6×10^3

9) 1.45×10^3

10) 9.1×10^4

11) 2×10^6

12) 6×10^{-7}

13) 3.54×10^5

14) 3.25×10^{-4}

15) 2.3×10^{-4}

16) 5.6×10^7

17) 2.1×10^4

18) 7.8×10^7

19) 2.2×10^{-6}

20) 1.2×10^{-4}

21) 2×10^{-2}

22) 8.8×10^6

23) 1.21×10^7

24) 1.8×10^{-1}

Square Roots

1) 1

2) 2

3) 3

4) 5

5) 4

6) 7

7) 6

8) 0

9) 8

10) 9

11) 11

12) 15

13) 12

14) 10

15) 16

16) 17

17) 18

18) 20

19) 30

20) 23

21) $3\sqrt{10}$

22) 32

23) $4\sqrt{3}$

24) $6\sqrt{3}$

25) $\sqrt{2}$

26) 9

27) $4\sqrt{5} + 5$

28) $13 - \sqrt{13}$

29) $9 - \sqrt{3}$

30) $12 + 2\sqrt{3}$

31) $17 - \sqrt{17}$

32) $6\sqrt{2}$

33) 3

34) $\frac{2}{3}$

Chapter 13:

Plane Figures

Topics that you'll learn in this part:

- ✓ Transformations: Translations, Rotations, and Reflections
- ✓ The Pythagorean Theorem
- ✓ Area of Triangles
- ✓ Perimeter of Polygons
- ✓ Area and Circumference of Circles
- ✓ Area of Squares, Rectangles, and Parallelograms
- ✓ Area of Trapezoids

Transformations: Translations, Rotations, and Reflections

✍ *Graph the image of the figure using the transformation given.*

1) translation: 4 units right and 1 unit down

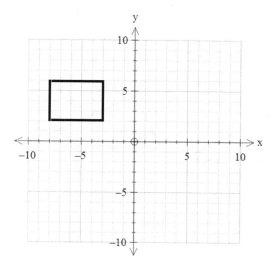

2) translation: 4 units left and 2 unit up

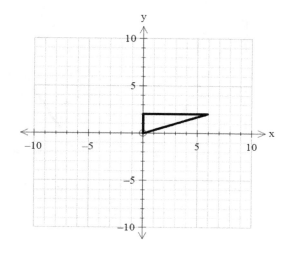

3) rotation 90∘ counterclockwise about the origin

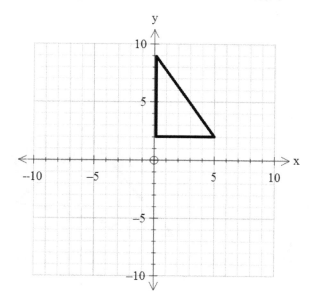

4) rotation 180∘ about the origin

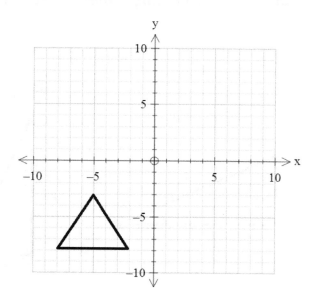

The Pythagorean Theorem

Do the following lengths form a right triangle?

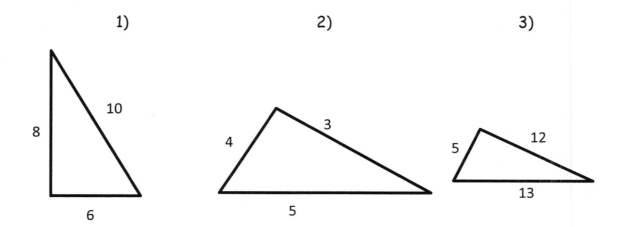

1)

2)

3)

Find each missing length to the nearest tenth.

4)

5)

6)

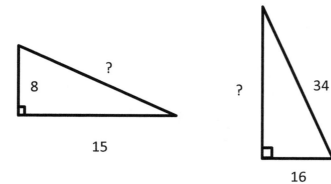

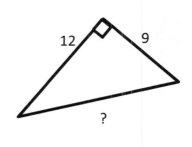

Area of Triangles

✎ *Find the area of each.*

1)

$c = 12\ mi$
$h = 4\ mi$

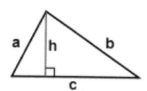

2)

$s = 15\ m$
$h = 9m$

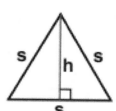

3)

$a = 5\ m$
$b = 11\ m$
$c = 14\ m$
$h = 4\ m$

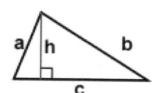

4)

$s = 10\ m$
$h = 8.6\ m$

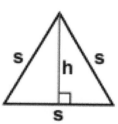

5)

$c = 15\ mi$
$h = 6\ mi$

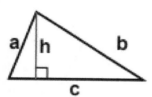

6)

$a = 5\ m$
$h = 4\ m$
$b = 9$
$C = 12$

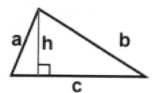

7)

$c = 8\ mi$
$h = 4\ mi$

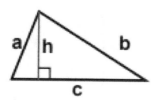

8)

$s = 10\ m$
$h = 8\ m$

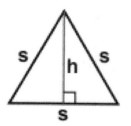

Perimeter of Polygon

✎*Find the perimeter of each shape.*

1)

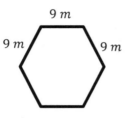

2)

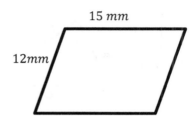

3)

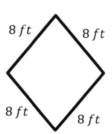

4)

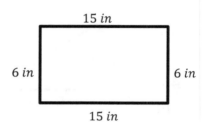

5)

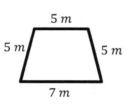

6)

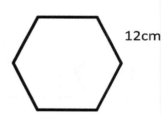

7)

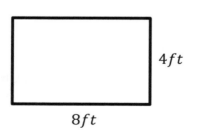

8)

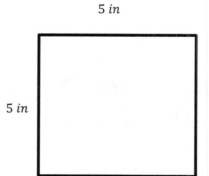

Area and Circumference of Circles

🖊 *Find the area and circumference of each.* ($\pi = 3.14$)

1)

4 *in*

2)

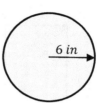

6 *in*

3)

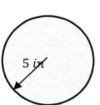

5 *in*

4)

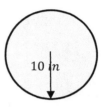

10 *in*

🖊 *Find the area and of each.* ($\pi = 3.14$)

5)

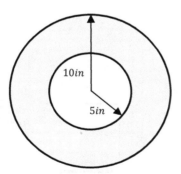

10*in*

5*in*

6)

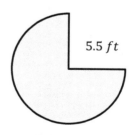

5.5 *ft*

7)

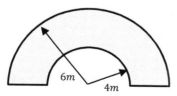

6*m*

4*m*

8)

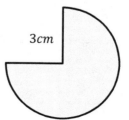

3*cm*

Area of Squares, Rectangles, and Parallelograms

🖎 *Find the area of each.*

1)

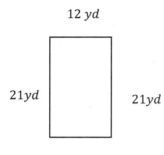

12 yd

21yd   21yd

12yd

2)

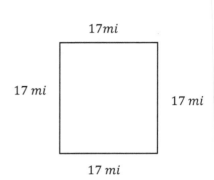

17mi

17 mi   17 mi

17 mi

3)

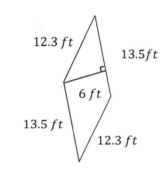

12.3 ft

13.5ft

6 ft

13.5 ft

12.3 ft

4)

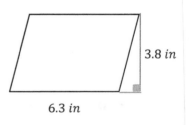

3.8 in

6.3 in

5)

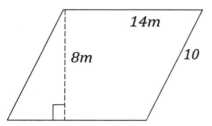

14m

8m   10

6)

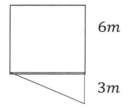

6m

3m

Area of Trapezoids

Calculate the area for each trapezoid.

1)

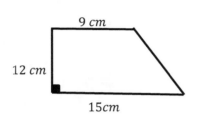

9 cm

12 cm

15cm

2)

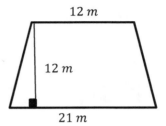

12 m

12 m

21 m

3)

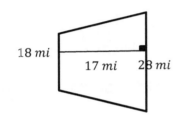

18 mi

17 mi 23 mi

4)

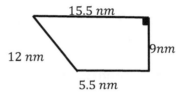

15.5 nm

9nm

12 nm

5.5 nm

5)

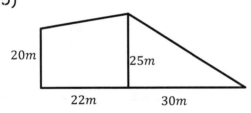

20m

25m

22m   30m

6)

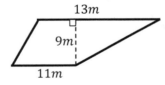

13m

9m

11m

7)

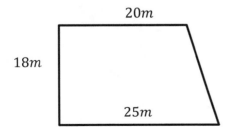

20m

18m

25m

8)

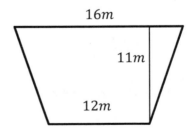

16m

11m

12m

Answers of Worksheets

Transformations

1) translation:

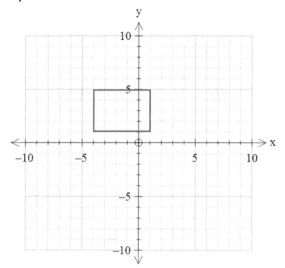

2) translation:

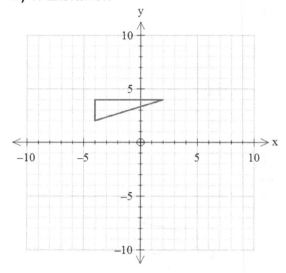

3) rotation 90∘ counterclockwise about the origin

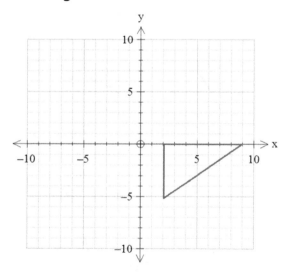

4) rotation 180∘ about the origin

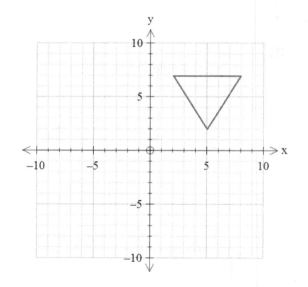

The Pythagorean Theorem

1) yes

2) yes

3) yes

4) 17

5) 30   **6)** 15

Area of Triangles

1) $24mi^2$ 3) $28\,m2$ 5) $45m^2$ 7) $16mi^2$
2) $67.5\,m2$ 4) $43\,m2$ 6) $24m^2$ 8) $40m^2$

Perimeter of Polygons

1) $54\,m$ 3) $32\,ft$ 5) $22m$ 7) $24ft$
2) $54\,mm$ 4) $42\,in$ 6) $72cm$ 8) $20in$

Area and Circumference of Circles

1) Area: $50.26\,in^2$, Circumference: $25.12\,in$
2) Area: $113.1in^2$, Circumference: $31.7in$
3) Area: $78.5in^2$, Circumference: $31.4\,in$
4) Area: $314.16in^2$, Circumference: $62.83in$
5) Area: $235.62in^2$
6) Area: $71.27\,ft^2$
7) Area: $31.415m^2$
8) Area: $21.2cm^2$

Area of Squares, Rectangles, and Parallelograms

1) $252\,yd^2$ 3) $81\,ft^2$ 5) $112m^2$
2) $289\,mi^2$ 4) $23.94\,in^2$ 6) $45m^2$

Area of Trapezoids

1) $144cm^2$ 3) $391\,mi^2$ 5) $870m^2$ 7) $405m^2$
2) $198\,m^2$ 4) $94.5\,nm^2$ 6) $108m^2$ 8) $154m^2$

Chapter 14:

Solid Figures

Topics that you'll learn in this part:

✓ Volume of Cubes and Rectangle Prisms

✓ Surface Area of Cubes

✓ Surface Area of a Prism

✓ Volume of Pyramids and Cones

✓ Surface Area of Pyramids and Cones

Volume of Cubes and Rectangle Prisms

✍ *Find the volume of each of the rectangular prisms.*

1)

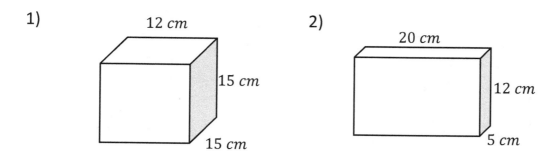

2)

✍ *Solve.*

3) Layla wants to build a wooden box with a volume of 45 cubic centimeters. She started with a width of 3cm. How long should Layla make the box?

4) The sea turtle habitat at the zoo is made by connecting two large aquariums. The first aquarium is 6m long, 4m wide, and 2m high. The second aquarium is 8m long, 9m wide, and 3m high. How many cubic meters of space do the sea turtles have in their habitat?

5) The closet is 6 feet wide, 5 feet deep and 8 feet tall. In the closet, there is a suitcase that is 2 feet wide, 3 feet long and 4 feet tall. How much room is left in the closet?

6) Find the volume of the rectangular prism.

Surface Area of Cubes

✍ *Find the surface of each cube.*

1)
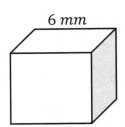
6 mm

2)
9 mm
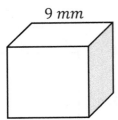

3)
10 cm
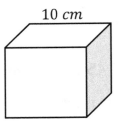

4)
12 mm
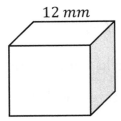

5)
30 mm
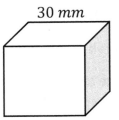

6)
15cm
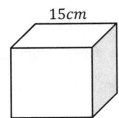

7)
6in
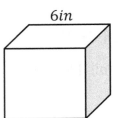

8)
12.5ft
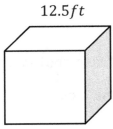

9)
13in
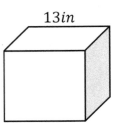

10)
9.5ft
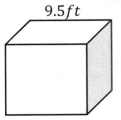

Surface Area of a Prism

✎ *Find the surface of each prism.*

1)

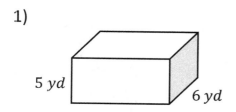

5 yd

6 yd

10 yd

2)

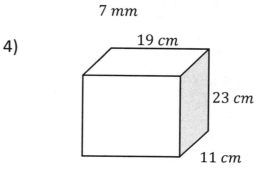

9 mm

7 mm

7 mm

3)

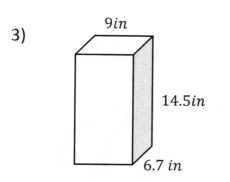

9in

14.5in

6.7 in

4)

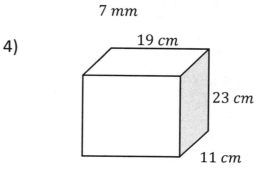

19 cm

23 cm

11 cm

5)

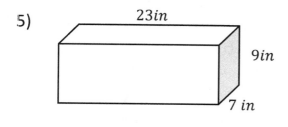

23in

9in

7 in

6)

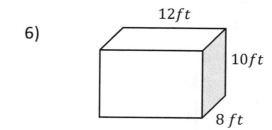

12ft

10ft

8 ft

7)

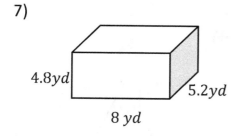

4.8yd

5.2yd

8 yd

8)

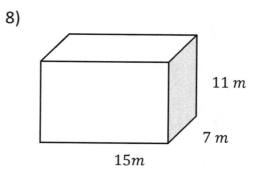

11 m

7 m

15m

Volume of Pyramids and Cones

✎ *Find the volume of each figure.* (π = 3.14)

1)

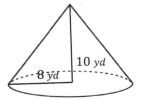

2)

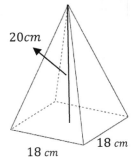

3)

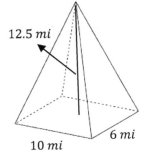

4)

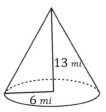

5)

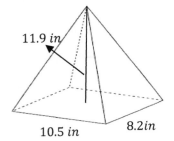

6)

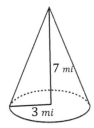

7)

8)

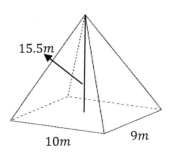

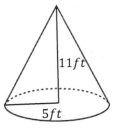

Answers of Worksheets

Volume of Cubes and Rectangle Prisms

1) $2,700 cm^3$

2) $1,200 cm^3$

3) 5

4) 264

5) 216

6) 140

Surface Area of a Cube

1) $216 \, mm^2$

2) $486 \, mm^2$

3) $600 \, cm^2$

4) $864 \, mm^2$

5) $5,400 \, mm^2$

6) $1,350 \, cm^2$

7) $216 \, in^2$

8) $937.5 \, ft^2$

9) $1,014 \, in^2$

10) $541.5 \, ft^2$

Surface Area of a Prism

1) $240 \, yd^2$

2) $350 \, mm^2$

3) $576.6 \, in^2$

4) $1,798 \, cm^2$

5) $736 \, in^2$

6) $592 \, ft^2$

7) $209.92 \, yd^2$

8) $694 \, m^2$

Volume of Pyramids and Cones

1) $670.2 \, yd^3$

2) $2,160 cm^3$

3) $250 mi^3$

4) $490.1 mi^3$

5) $341.5 in^3$

6) $65.97 mi^3$

7) $465 m^3$

8) $288 ft^3$

Chapter 15:

Statistics

Topics that you'll learn in this part:

✓ Mean, Median, Mode, and Range of the Given Data

✓ First Quartile, Second Quartile and Third Quartile of the Given Data

✓ Bar Graph

✓ Box and Whisker Plots

✓ Stem–And–Leaf Plot

✓ The Pie Graph or Circle Graph

✓ Scatter Plots

Mean, Median, Mode, and Range of the Given Data

✏️ *Find Mean, Median, Mode, and Range of the Given Data.*

1) 7, 2, 5, 1, 1, 2,3,4

2) 2, 2, 2, 3, 6, 3, 7, 4

3) 9, 4, 3, 1, 7, 9, 4, 6, 4

4) 8, 4, 2, 4, 3, 2, 4, 5

5) 8, 5, 7, 5, 7, 9, 8,8,6

6) 5, 1, 4, 4, 9, 2, 9,1, 2, 5, 1,8

7) 4, 7, 5, 9,5,7, 7, 7, 5, 2, 3, 5

8) 7, 5, 4, 9, 6, 7, 7, 5, 2,8

9) 2, 5, 5, 6, 2, 4, 7, 6, 4, 9,5

10) 10, 5, 2, 5, 4, 5, 8, 10,8

11) 4,5, 2, 2,6,8,10,12

12) 5, 9, 5, 9,8,6,11,9,6,8

13) 14,16,16,15,19,16

14) 10,9,12,13,13,17,15,10

15) 3,2,9,8,5,5,6,8

16) 14,16,18,17,12,16,15,16

17) 9,18,17,15,14,19,18,17

18) 15,12,18,17,15,15,12,14

19) 32,51,38,69,15,50,38,8

20) 1,9,8,6,5,9,8,9

✏️ *Solve.*

21) A stationery sold 14 pencils, 40 red pens, 50 blue pens, 10 notebooks, 16 erasers, 38 rulers and 36 color pencils. What are the Mode and Range for the stationery sells?

22) In an English test, eight students score 14,13,17,11,19,20,14 and 15. What are their Median, Mode and Range?

23) Bob has 12 black pen, 14 red pen, 15 green pens, 24 blue pens and 3 boxes of yellow pens. If the Mean and Median are 16 and 15 respectively, what is the number of yellow pens in each box?

Box and Whisker Plot

✍ *Make box and whisker plots for the given data.*

1) 11,17,22,18,23,2,3,16,21,7,8,15,5

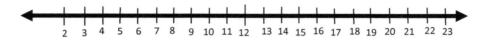

2) 33,31,30,38,40,36

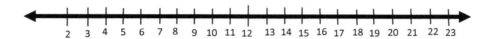

3) 46,36,15,21,65,25,48,70,68

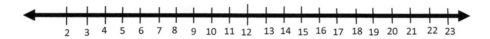

4) 9,10,12,15,17,19,24,26,28

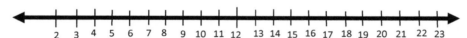

5) 41,43,45,47,51,50,44

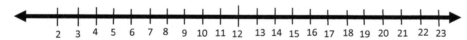

6) 60,66,62,65,68,70,72

7) 72,82,81,76,77,82,84,79,80

Bar Graph

✍️ *Graph the given information as a bar graph.*

1) The number of bed-sheets manufactured by a factory during five consecutive weeks is given below. Draw the bar graph representing the above data.

week	First	Second	Third	Fourth	Fifth
Number of bed-sheets	550	810	680	320	850

2) The number of students in 7 different classes is given below. Represent this data on the bar graph.

class	6th	7th	8th	9th	10th	11th	12th
Number of students	125	115	130	140	145	100	80

3) The number of trees planted by Eco-club of a school in different years is given below. Draw the bar graph to represent the data.

Year	2005	2006	2007	2008	2009	2010
Number of trees to be planted	150	220	350	400	300	380

4) The following data represents the sale of refrigerator sets in a showroom in first 6 months of the year. Draw the bar graph for the data given and find out the months in which the sale was minimum and maximum.

Months	Jan	Feb	March	April	May	June
No. of refrigerator sold	19	21	12	46	35	28

Stem–And–Leaf Plot

🖎 *Make stem ad leaf plots for the given data.*

1) 74,88,97,72,79,86,95,79,83,91

Stem	Leaf plot

2) 37,48,26,33,49,26,19,26,48

Stem	Leaf plot

3) A zookeeper created the following stem-and-leaf plot showing the number of tigers at each major zoo in the country. What was the smallest number of tigers at any one zoo?

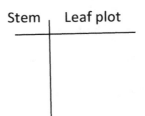

Stem	Leaf plot
0	7
1	1 4 8
2	5 5 5 6 7 7 9
3	
4	

4) The government published the following stem-and-leaf plot showing the number of bears at each major zoo in the country. How many zoos have more than 50 bears?

Stem	Leaf plot
0	
1	8 8
2	1 3 6 6 7 7 9
3	1 7
4	1 4 5 7
5	0 3

The Pie Graph or Circle Graph

✎*Solve.*

1) Suppose you take a poll of the students in your class to find out their favorite foods, and get the following results:

Pizza:41%, Ice Cream:24%, Raw Mushrooms:9%, Dog Food:11%, Chicken Livers:15%

Organize this data in a circle graph.

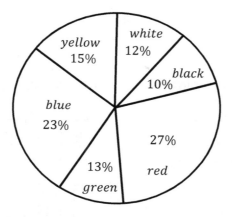

Favorite colors

2) Which color is the most?

3) What percentage of pie graph is yellow?

4) Which color is the least?

5) What percentage of pie graph is blue?

6) What percentage of pie graph is green?

Scatter Plots

✍ Construct a scatter plot.

1) Construct a graph of the length of the humerus bone vs. the length of the radius.

Length of Radius (cm)	25	22	23.5	22.5	23	22.6	21.4	21.9	23.5	24.3	24
Length of Humerus (cm)	29.7	26.5	27.1	26	28	25.2	24	23.8	26.7	29	27

2) Plot the data on the scatter plot below, choosing appropriate scales and labels.

Age	25	30	35	37	38	40	41	45	55	60	62	65	70	75
Earnings ($)	22000	26500	29500	29000	30000	32000	35000	36000	41000	41000	42500	43000	37000	37500

3) The table shows the numbers of students remaining on an after-school bus and the numbers of minutes since leaving the school.

Minutes	0	5	9	15	23	26	32
Number of students	56	45	39	24	17	6	0

Plot the data from the table on the graph. Describe the relationship between the two data sets.

Answers of Worksheets

Mean, Median, Mode, and Range of the Given Data

1)   mean: 3.125, median: 2.5, mode: 1, 2, range: 6

2)   mean: 3.625, median: 3, mode: 2, range: 5

3)   mean: 5.22, median: 4, mode: 4, range: 8

4)   mean: 4, median: 4, mode: 4, range: 6

5)   mean: 7, median: 7, mode: 5, 7, 8, range: 4

6)   mean: 4.25, median: 4, mode: 1, range: 8

7)   mean: 5.5, median: 5, mode: 7.5, range: 7

8)   mean: 6, median: 6.5, mode: 7, range: 7

9)   mean: 5, median: 5, mode: 5, range: 7

10)   mean: 6.33, median: 5, mode: 5, range: 8

11)   mean: 6.125, median: 2, mode: 2, range: 10

12)   mean: 7.6, median:8, mode: 9, range: 6

13)   mean: 16, median:16, mode: 16, range: 5

14)   mean: 12.375, median:12.5, mode: 10,13, range: 8

15)   mean: 5.75, median:5.5, mode:8,5, range: 7

16)   mean: 15.5, median:16, mode: 16, range: 6

17)   mean: 15.875, median:17, mode: 18,17, range: 10

18)   mean: 14.75, median:15, mode: 15, range: 6

19)   mean: 37.625, median:38, mode: 38, range: 61

20)   mean: 6.875, median:8, mode: 9, range: 8

21) Mode: none, range:40

22) median:14.5, mode:14, range:9

23) 5

Box and Whisker Plots

1)

2)

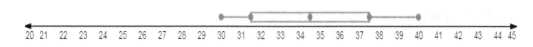

3)

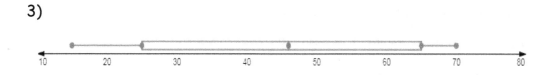

4)

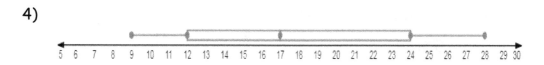

5)

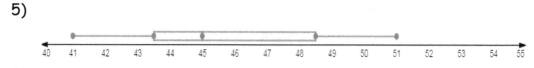

6)

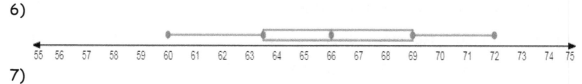

7)

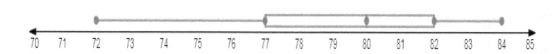

Bar Graph

1)

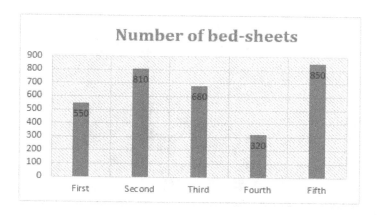

2)

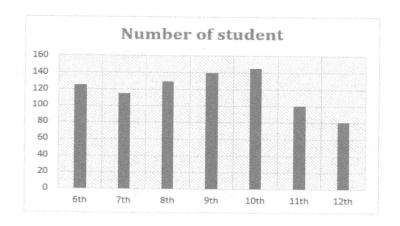

3)

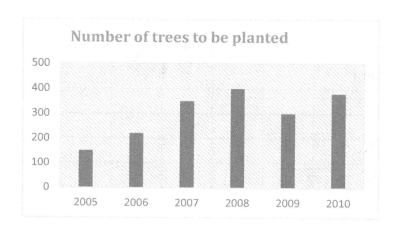

4)

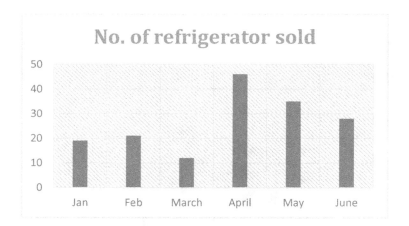

Stem–And–Leaf Plot

1)

Stem	leaf
7	2 4 9 9
8	3 6 8
9	1 5 7

2)

Stem	leaf
1	9
2	6 6 6
3	3 7
4	8 8 9

3)

Stem	leaf
4	1 2
5	3 4 4 8
6	5 5 7 9

4) 7

5) 1

The Pie Graph or Circle Graph

1)

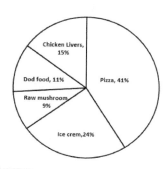

2) red

3) 15%

4) black

5) 23%

6) 13%

Scatter Plots

1)

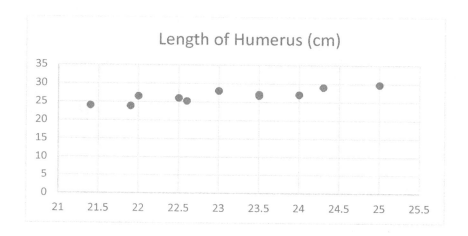

2)

3)

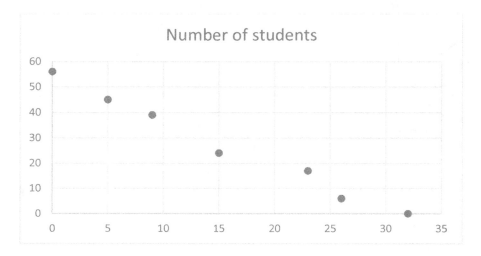

When time increase, number of students decrease

Chapter 16:

Probability

Topics that you'll learn in this part:

- ✓ Probability of Simple Events
- ✓ Experimental Probability
- ✓ Independent and Dependent Events Word Problems
- ✓ Factorials
- ✓ Permutations
- ✓ Combination

Probability of Simple Events

🖎 *Solve.*

1) A number is chosen at random from 1 to 50. Find the probability of selecting multiples of 10.

2) You spin the spinner shown below once. Each sector shown has an equal area. What is P (shaded sector)?

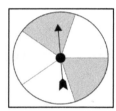

3) You draw a card at random from a deck that contains 3 black cards and 7 red cards. What is the probability of choosing a black card?

4) Greg has an MP3 player called the Jumble. The Jumble randomly selects a song for the user to listen to. Greg's Jumble has 6 classical songs, 7 rock songs, and 9 rap songs on it. What is P (not a rap song)?

5) Omar ordered his sister a birthday card from a company that randomly selects a card from their inventory. The company has 21 total cards in inventory.14 of those cards are birthday cards. What is P (not a birthday card)?

6) Giovanna owns a farm. She is going to randomly select one animal to present at the state fair. She has 6 pigs, 7 chickens, and 10 cows. What is What is the probability of choosing a chicken?

Experimental Probability

✎*Solve.*

1) A bag contains 18 balls: two green, five black, eight blue, a brown, a red and one white. If 17 balls are removed from the bag at random, what is the probability that a brown ball has been removed?

A. $\frac{1}{9}$ C. $\frac{16}{17}$

B. $\frac{1}{6}$ D. $\frac{17}{18}$

2) The table shows the number of feathers Patsy the Peacock sold at each of the 8 festivals this year. Based on this data, what is a reasonable estimate of the probability that Patsy sells fewer than 5 feathers next festival?

3	6	1	4
2	3	7	2

3) The Cinemania theater showed 108 different movies last year. Of those, 15 movies were action movies. Based on this data, what is a reasonable estimate of the probability that the next movie is an action movie?

4) Stephen read 12 books, 20 magazines, and 17 newspaper articles last year. Based on this data, what is a reasonable estimate of the probability that Stephen's next reading material is a magazine?

5) March Madness Movies served 23 lemonades out of a total of 111 fountain drinks last weekend. Based on this data, what is a reasonable estimate of the probability that the next fountain drink ordered is a lemonade?

Factorials

✍ *Determine the value for each expression*

1) $\frac{9!}{6!}$ 3) $\frac{7!}{3!}$ 5) $\frac{6!+2!}{4!}$

2) $\frac{10!}{8!}$ 4) $\frac{5!}{4!}$ 6) $3! \times 4!$

✍ *Solve.*

7) While playing Scrabble®, you need to make a word out of the letters A N P S. How many arrangements of these letters are possible?

8) How many ways can you have your quarter pound hamburger prepared if you can have it prepared with or without mustard, ketchup, mayonnaise, lettuce, tomatoes, pickles, cheese, and onions?

9) How many arrangements of all the letters in the word PYRAMID do not end with D?

10) Five students are running for Junior Class President. They must give speeches before the election committee. In how many different orders could they give their speeches?

11) How many five-letter "words" can be formed from the letters in the word COMBINE?

12) In how many ways can six different algebra books and three different geometry books be arranged on a shelf if all the books of one subject must remain together?

Combination and Permutations

✍ *Solve.*

1) In how many ways can we select a chairman, vice-chairman, secretary, and treasurer from a group of 10 persons?

2) You have been asked to judge an art contest with 15 entries. In how many ways can you assign 1st, 2nd and 3rd place? (Express your answer as P (n, k) for some n and k and evaluate.)

3) How many three letter words (including nonsense words) can you make from the letters of the English alphabet, if letters cannot be repeated? (Express your answer as P (n, k) for some n and k and evaluate.)

4) Five students are to be chosen from a class of 10 and lined up for a photograph. How many such photographs can be taken?

5) You have 6 reindeer, Prancer, Rudy, Balthazar, Quentin, Jebediah, and Lancer, and you want to have 3 fly your sleigh. You always have your reindeer fly in a single-file line. How many ways can you arrange your reindeer?

6) A committee of 5 people is to be chosen from a group of 6 men and 4 women. How many committees are possible if there are no restrictions?

7) In a hand of poker, 5 cards are dealt from a regular pack of 52 cards. What is the total possible number of hands if there are no restrictions?

8) You just got a free ticket for a boat ride, and you can bring along 2 friends! Unfortunately, you have 5 friends who want to come along. How many different groups of friends could you take with you?

9) Christopher is packing his bags for his vacation. He has 8 unique shirts, but only 5 fit in his bag. How many different groups of 5 shirts can he take?

Answers of Worksheets

Probability of simple events

1) $\frac{5}{10}$ 2) $\frac{2}{5}$ 3) $\frac{3}{10}$ 4) $\frac{13}{22}$ 5) $\frac{7}{21}$ 6) $\frac{1}{23}$

Experimental Probability

1) $\frac{17}{18}$ 2) 0.75   3) $\frac{15}{108}$ 4) $\frac{20}{49}$ 5) $\frac{23}{111}$

Factorials

1) 504
2) 90
3) 840

4) 5
5) 30.08
6) 144

7) 24
8) 256
9) 4320

10) 120
11) 2520
12) 720

Combination and Permutations

1) 5040
2) 2730
3) 15600

4) 30240
5) 120
6) 252

7) 2598960
8) 10
9) 56

Chapter 17:

Complex Numbers

Topics that you'll practice in this chapter:

- ✓ Adding and Subtracting Complex Numbers

- ✓ Multiplying and Dividing Complex Numbers

- ✓ Graphing Complex Numbers

- ✓ Rationalizing Imaginary Denominators

Adding and Subtracting Complex Numbers

✍ *Simplify.*

1) $(7i) - (3i) =$

2) $(4i) + (9i) =$

3) $(2i) + (10i) =$

4) $(8i) - (7i) =$

5) $(3i) + (10i) =$

6) $(5i) - (-3i) + 2 =$

7) $(-11i) + (-4i) =$

8) $(17i) - (-6i) =$

9) $(3 - 5i) - (8i) =$

10) $(9i) + (7 + i) =$

11) $(6 - 5i) + (-3i) =$

12) $(-4i) + (1 + 2i) =$

13) $8 + (4 - 6i) =$

14) $(-12i) - (-2 + 2i) =$

15) $(3 + 4i) - (-2i) =$

16) $(1 + 9i) + (-6i) =$

17) $(3i) - (-3i + 4) =$

18) $(4i - 7) + (-9i) =$

19) $(-9i) - (12 - 3i) =$

20) $(4 - 5i) + (7 + 2i) =$

21) $(3 - 3i) + (5 + 5i) =$

22) $(14 + 2i) - (1 + 2i) =$

23) $(-5 - 3i) - (-6 - 8i) =$

24) $(-6 + 8i) - (-4 + 2i) =$

25) $(-10 + i) - (-17 - 5i) =$

26) $(-14 - 2i) + (3 + 9i) =$

27) $(-16 - 7i) + (-7 - 3i) =$

28) $-9 + (4i) + (-9 + 2i) =$

29) $15 - (3i) + (5 - 16i) =$

30) $-3 + (-9 + 8i) - 2 =$

31) $(-14i) + (1 + i) + 1 =$

32) $(-7i) - (3 - 6i) + 5i =$

Multiplying and Dividing Complex Numbers

✎ *Simplify.*

1) $(i)(-i) =$

2) $(-3i)(2i) =$

3) $(2i)(3i)(-4i) =$

4) $(6i)(-7i) =$

5) $(-1 - 2i)(1 + 2i) =$

6) $(4 - 3i)^2 =$

7) $(2 - 6i)(1 - 4i) =$

8) $(4 + i)^2 =$

9) $(5i)(-2\ i)(3 - 6i) =$

10) $(4 - 4i)(2 + 3i) =$

11) $(7 + i)(5 - 5i) =$

12) $(6 - 3i)(4 - 6i) =$

13) $3(3i) + (4i)(5 + 7i) =$

14) $\dfrac{2}{-16i} =$

15) $\dfrac{6-3i}{-3i} =$

16) $\dfrac{8+12i}{2i} =$

17) $\dfrac{4i}{-3+4i} =$

18) $\dfrac{-4-16i}{-8i} =$

19) $\dfrac{18i}{6-3i} =$

20) $\dfrac{1+i}{3-4i} =$

21) $\dfrac{4+5i}{-1+4i} =$

22) $\dfrac{-3-4i}{-2+5i} =$

23) $\dfrac{-7+2i}{-4-i} =$

24) $\dfrac{8+3i}{4+2i} =$

25) $\dfrac{6+3i}{2-i} =$

Graphing Complex Numbers

✎ *Identify each complex number graphed.*

1)

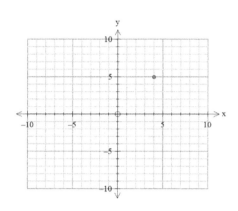

2)

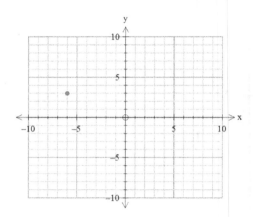

3)

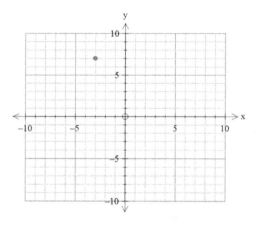

4)

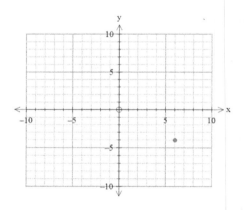

Rationalizing Imaginary Denominators

✍ *Simplify.*

1) $\dfrac{4}{2i} =$

2) $\dfrac{-6}{8i} =$

3) $\dfrac{-12}{-i} =$

4) $\dfrac{-9}{-3i} =$

5) $\dfrac{4}{7i} =$

6) $\dfrac{12}{-5i} =$

7) $\dfrac{8}{-6i} =$

8) $\dfrac{-15}{12i} =$

9) $\dfrac{2a}{5bi} =$

10) $\dfrac{6+2i}{-3i} =$

11) $\dfrac{7-i}{-5i} =$

12) $\dfrac{9+12i}{-7i} =$

13) $\dfrac{15i}{3+2i} =$

14) $\dfrac{-4i}{-3-7i} =$

15) $\dfrac{-5-5i}{-3+3i} =$

16) $\dfrac{-2+2i}{6-4i} =$

17) $\dfrac{7-3i}{5-3i} =$

18) $\dfrac{-2+i}{-2-i} =$

19) $\dfrac{-10+i}{-i} =$

20) $\dfrac{12+i}{4-5i} =$

21) $\dfrac{-5-4i}{-5i} =$

22) $\dfrac{4-i}{3+6i} =$

23) $\dfrac{10-5i}{2+4i} =$

24) $\dfrac{-3i+5}{-4-i} =$

Answers of Worksheets

Adding and Subtracting Complex Numbers

1) $4i$

2) $13i$

3) $12i$

4) i

5) $13i$

6) $8i + 2$

7) $-15i$

8) $23i$

9) $3 - 13i$

10) $7 + 10i$

11) $6 - 8i$

12) $1 - 2i$

13) $12 - 6i$

14) $2 - 14i$

15) $3 + 6i$

16) $1 + 3i$

17) $-4 + 6i$

18) $-7 - 5i$

19) $-12 - 6i$

20) $11 - 3i$

21) $8 + 2i$

22) 13

23) $1 + 5i$

24) $-2 + 6i$

25) $7 + 6i$

26) $-11 + 7i$

27) $-23 - 10i$

28) $-18 + 6i$

29) $20 - 19i$

30) $-14 + 8i$

31) $2 - 13i$

32) $-3 + 4i$

Multiplying and Dividing Complex Numbers

1) 1

2) 6

3) $24i$

4) 42

5) $3 - 4i$

6) $7 - 24i$

7) $-22 - 14i$

8) $15 + 8i$

9) $30 - 60i$

10) $20 + 4i$

11) $40 + 30i$

12) $6 - 48i$

13) $-28 + 29i$

14) $\frac{i}{8}$

15) $1 + 2i$

16) $6 - 4i$

17) $\frac{16}{25} - \frac{12}{25}i$

18) $2 - \frac{1}{2}i$

19) $-\frac{6}{5} + \frac{12}{5}i$

20) $\frac{-1}{25} + \frac{7}{25}i$

21) $\frac{16}{17} - \frac{21}{17}i$

22) $-\frac{14}{29} + \frac{23}{29}i$

23) $\frac{26}{17} - \frac{15}{17}i$

24) $\frac{19}{10} - \frac{1}{5}i$

25) $\frac{9}{5} + \frac{12}{5}i$

Graphing Complex Numbers

1) $4 + 5i$

2) $-6 + 3i$

3) $-3 + 7i$

4) $6 - 4i$

Rationalizing Imaginary Denominators

1) $-2i$

2) $\frac{3}{4}i$

3) $-12i$

4) $-3i$

5) $-\frac{4}{7}i$

6) $\frac{12}{5}i$

7) $\frac{8}{6}i$

8) $\frac{5}{4}i$

9) $\frac{2a}{5b}i$

10) $-\frac{2}{3} + 2i$

11) $\frac{1}{5} + \frac{7}{5}i$

12) $-\frac{12}{7} + \frac{9}{7}i$

13) $\frac{30}{13} + \frac{45}{13}i$

14) $\frac{14}{29} + \frac{6}{29}i$

15) $\frac{15}{6}i$

16) $-\frac{5}{13} + \frac{1}{13}i$

17) $\frac{22}{17} + \frac{3}{17}i$

18) $\frac{3}{5} - \frac{4}{5}i$

19) $-1 - 10i$

20) $\frac{43}{41} + \frac{64}{41}i$

21) $\frac{4}{5} - i$

22) $\frac{6}{45} - \frac{27}{45}i$

23) $-2i$

24) $-1 + i$

Chapter 18:

Logarithms

Topics that you'll practice in this chapter:

- ✓ Rewriting Logarithms
- ✓ Evaluating Logarithms
- ✓ Properties of Logarithms
- ✓ Natural Logarithms
- ✓ Exponential Equations Requiring Logarithms
- ✓ Solving Logarithmic Equations

Rewriting Logarithms

 Rewrite each equation in exponential form.

1) $log_3 27 = 3$

2) $log_{\frac{1}{5}} \frac{1}{25} = 2$

3) $log_4 64 = 3$

4) $log_7 \frac{1}{49} = -2$

5) $log_{\frac{1}{8}} 512 = -3$

6) $log_{\frac{2}{3}} \frac{16}{81} = 4$

7) $log_{16} 4 = \frac{1}{2}$

8) $log_{64} \frac{1}{8} = -\frac{1}{2}$

9) $log_5 3125 = 5$

10) $log_6 216 = 3$

11) $log_{\frac{1}{10}} 10000 = -4$

12) $log_{\frac{1}{7}} 343 = -3$

13) $log_2 1024 = 10$

14) $log_3 \frac{1}{81} = -4$

15) $log_{\frac{2}{5}} \sqrt{\frac{2}{5}} = \frac{1}{2}$

16) $log_{\frac{2}{10}} 625 = -4$

17) $log_4 \frac{1}{1024} = -5$

18) $log_{\frac{7}{10}} \frac{1000}{343} = -3$

19) $log_{\frac{3}{8}} \frac{27}{512} = 3$

20) $log_{\frac{3}{5}} \frac{25}{9} = -2$

 Rewrite each exponential equation in logarithmic form.

21) $\left(\frac{1}{5}\right)^{\frac{1}{2}} = \frac{1}{\sqrt{5}}$

22) $\left(\frac{1}{3}\right)^3 = \frac{1}{9}$

23) $\left(\frac{4}{7}\right)^{-2} = \frac{49}{16}$

24) $7^4 = 2401$

25) $\left(\frac{2}{5}\right)^{-3} = \frac{125}{8}$

26) $\left(\frac{5}{4}\right)^{\frac{1}{2}} = \frac{\sqrt{5}}{2}$

27) $12^2 = 144$

28) $\left(\frac{9}{8}\right)^3 = \frac{729}{512}$

29) $6^{-3} = \frac{1}{216}$

30) $(100)^{\frac{1}{2}} = 10$

31) $125^{-\frac{1}{3}} = \frac{1}{5}$

32) $6^{-5} = \frac{1}{7776}$

33) $\left(\frac{25}{9}\right)^{-\frac{1}{2}} = \frac{3}{5}$

34) $\left(\frac{7}{11}\right)^{-2} = \frac{121}{49}$

Evaluating Logarithms

✎ *Evaluate each logarithm.*

1) $\log_3 27 =$

2) $\log_{\frac{1}{5}} 3125 =$

3) $\log_4 \frac{1}{2} =$

4) $\log_{\frac{1}{3}} 81 =$

5) $\log_{\frac{2}{3}} \sqrt{\frac{3}{2}} =$

6) $\log_7 \frac{7^{\frac{3}{4}}}{7} =$

7) $\log_{\frac{3}{2}} \frac{32}{243} =$

8) $\log_5 \frac{5^{\frac{2}{3}}}{5} =$

9) $\log_{\frac{2}{7}} \frac{8}{343} =$

10) $\log_{15} \frac{1}{3375} =$

11) $\log_{11} \frac{1}{121} =$

12) $\log_{17} \frac{1}{289} =$

13) $\log_{\frac{1}{9}} 3 =$

14) $\log_4 8 =$

15) $\log_6 6^{\frac{2}{5}} =$

16) $\log_{25} 1 =$

17) $\log_2 \frac{1}{32} =$

18) $\log_7 \frac{\sqrt{7}}{2401} =$

✎ *Circle the points which are on the graph of the given logarithmic functions.*

19) $y = \log_2(x + 1) - 3$ $(2, 4),$ $(8, 4),$ $(0, -3)$

20) $y = 2\log_5(2x - 2)$ $(3, 6),$ $(\frac{3}{2}, 0),$ $(\frac{1}{3}, 2)$

21) $y = 2\log_2(x + 1) + 1$ $(3, 5),$ $(2, 1),$ $(5, 5)$

22) $y = -4\log_5(2x + 1) - 7$ $(1, 7),$ $(2, -11),$ $(4, 8)$

23) $y = 3\log_7(4x + 9) + 5$ $(-2, 0),$ $(1, 2),$ $(10, 11)$

24) $y = \log_3 3(2x - 1) + 4$ $(5, 7),$ $(8, 8),$ $(4, 4)$

25) $y = \log_4(3x + 4) - 2\log_4 x$ $(3, 3),$ $(4, 0),$ $(0, 4)$

Properties of Logarithms

✍ *Expand each logarithm.*

1) $log\ (25 \times 18) =$

2) $log\ (30 \times 12) =$

3) $log\ (9 \times 8) =$

4) $log\ (\frac{10}{27}) =$

5) $log\ (\frac{6}{15}) =$

6) $log\ (\frac{41}{29})^{-3} =$

7) $log\ (11^{-2} \times 6^2) =$

8) $log\ (\frac{16}{9})^{-2} =$

9) $log\left(\frac{6^3}{13}\right)^{-2} =$

10) $log\ (3x \times y^{-2})^5 =$

11) $log\left(x^2 \times y^{\frac{1}{2}} \times z^5\right) =$

12) $log\left(\frac{(a+b)^4}{c}\right) =$

13) $log\left(\frac{3q}{r^3}\right) =$

✍ *Condense each expression to a single logarithm.*

14) $log\ 15 - 2log\ 2 =$

15) $3log\ 7 + log\ 9 =$

16) $-2\ log\ 8 + 3\ log\ 7 =$

17) $5\ log\ 15 - 3\ log\ 6 =$

18) $-2\ log\ 14 + 5\ log\ 14 =$

19) $11\ log\ 11 - 3log\ 7 =$

20) $log\ 13 - 4\ log\ 4 =$

21) $7log\ 5 - 4log\ 16 =$

22) $17log\ 2 + 6log\ 5 =$

23) $log_7\ 7x + 7\ log_7\ 9y =$

24) $4log_5\ 3k - 3\ log_5\ 4g =$

25) $log_8\ 6r - 2\ log_8\ 2s =$

26) $3\ log_3\ 2u + 3\ log_3\ 4v =$

27) $6\ log_2\ 4w - 11\ log_2\ u =$

Natural Logarithms

Solve each equation for x.

1) $e^x = 10$

2) $e^x = 12$

3) $e^x = 13$

4) $ln\ x = -3$

5) $ln\ (ln\ x) = 3$

6) $e^x = 14$

7) $ln(3x + 6) = 9$

8) $ln(x + 2) = 3$

9) $ln(4x - 2) = 8$

10) $ln\ 2x = \frac{1}{4}$

11) $ln5x = 2e^3$

12) $ln\ x = ln\ 5 + ln\ 8$

13) $ln\ x = 2ln\ 9 + ln\ 12$

Evaluate without using a calculator.

14) $ln\ \frac{2^2}{4} =$

15) $ln\ e^{-5} =$

16) $2\ln e =$

17) $ln\ 3e^{-2} =$

18) $-2ln\ e =$

19) $ln\left(\frac{1}{e^3}\right) =$

20) $2e^{ln4} =$

21) $e^{-2ln5} =$

22) $2e^{2ln6} =$

23) $ln\ e^{\frac{2}{3}} =$

Reduce the following expressions to simplest form.

24) $e^{ln10+3ln2} =$

25) $e^{-2ln\left(\frac{2}{e}\right)} =$

26) $-ln(e^2) =$

27) $ln\left(\frac{1}{e}\right)^{-4} =$

28) $e^{2ln2+4ln2} =$

29) $e^{ln\left(\frac{2}{3e}\right)} =$

30) $2\ ln(1^{-3e}) =$

31) $3ln\left(\frac{1}{e}\right)^{-5} =$

32) $2ln\left(\frac{2\sqrt{e}}{e}\right) =$

33) $e^{-4lne+3ln3} =$

34) $e^{ln\frac{3}{e}} =$

35) $-2\ ln(e^0) =$

Exponential Equations and Logarithms

 Solve each equation for the unknown variable.

1) $2^{3n} = 64$

2) $3^{2x} = 81$

3) $5^{2n+1} = 3125$

4) $7^{r-1} = 1$

5) $1296^x = 6$

6) $5^{x+1} = 625$

7) $2^{3x+4} = 1024$

8) $7^n = 106.7$

9) $\frac{80^{2a}}{25^a} = 16$

10) $32 \times 2^{-v} = 4$

11) $9^{2n-2} = \frac{1}{81}$

12) $\left(\frac{2}{9}\right)^n = \frac{81}{4}$

13) $256^{x-1} = 4$

14) $7^{8-5x} = 7^{-x}$

15) $8^{3x+5} = 8^{x-1}$

16) $256^{2n} = 16$

17) $11^{5x-1} = 11^{-x+5}$

18) $5^{5n} = 125$

19) $4^{-5k} = 256$

20) $8^{6x-3} = 8^{2x+1}$

21) $2^{-2m} \times 2^m = 2^{32}$

22) $3^{3x-1} = 243$

23) $144^{-x}/24 = 864$

24) $\frac{81}{3^{4x}} = 9^{-x}$

25) $4^{3a^2} \times 4^{a+1} = 4^{3a^2+6}$

26) $13^{3n} \times 13^{n-4} = 13^{3n+24}$

 Solve each problem. (Round to the nearest whole number)

27) A substance decays 12% each day. After 10 days, there are 8 milligrams of the substance remaining. How many milligrams were there initially? _____

28) A culture of bacteria grows continuously. The culture doubles every 4 hours. If the initial amount of bacteria is 15, how many bacteria will there be in 17 hours? _____

29) Bob plans to invest $4,700 at an annual rate of 6.5%. How much will Bob have in the account after four years if the balance is compounded quarterly? _____

30) Suppose you plan to invest $7,000 at an annual rate of 4.5%. How much will you have in the account after 6 years if the balance is compounded monthly? _____

Solving Logarithmic Equations

 Find the value of the variables in each equation.

1) $3log_5 25 - 2x + 3 = 0$

2) $-2log_3 4x = 2$

3) $3 log_7 5x + 4 = 7$

4) $3x + log_2 32 = 5x$

5) $log_3 2x - log_2 16 = log_5 25$

6) $12x + log_{12} 144 = 3$

7) $log_5 (x + 5) + 2 = 3$

8) $log_7 (4x + 3) + 3 = log_7 49$

9) $log_2 (x^2 - 6x) = 3 + log_2 (1 - x)$

10) $log_2 (5x + 2) + log_2 16 = log_2 (3x + 2)$

11) $x^2 - 4log_2 8 + x = 0$

12) $log_5 (2x + 5) = 2log_5 (x + 1)$

13) $log_6 (7x - 4) = log_6 (2x + 1)$

14) $log_8 (x^2) + log_8 64 = 2$

15) $log_3 (x^2 + 4) = log_3 (4x)$

16) $2log_4 (x + 1) = log_4 (x + 3)$

17) $-2log_8 8x - 2log_8 2x = log_8 1$

18) $6x + log_3 27 - 2 = 0$

 Find the value of x in each natural logarithm equation.

19) $2 ln(x + 1) - ln(x + 1) = 1$

20) $ln(2x + 1) - ln 4x = ln 12$

21) $2ln(x + 2) = ln(x + 2)$

22) $ln(3x + 3) - ln 15 = 0$

23) $ln(x + 2) + ln(x - 1) = ln 4$

24) $ln(10x + 5) + ln15 = ln 30$

25) $2ln(2x - 2) = ln16$

26) $ln(x + 3) - ln(x - 5) = ln 2$

27) $ln(8x + 5) - ln(1 - 2x) = -ln2$

28) $ln(x^2 - 2x) - lnx = ln8$

29) $ln(m^2 - 1) - ln(m + 1) = ln 3$

30) $ln(a^3 - a^2) - ln2a^2 = ln 4$

31) $ln(x^2 + 4x + 4) - 2 ln(x + 2) = ln2x$

32) $ln3x + lnx == ln(2x^2 + 4) - ln2$

33) $ln(-2x + 4) = ln 6$

34) $-3 ln 2x + ln x^3 = ln x$

35) $4 ln(2x - 1) - 3 ln(2x - 1) = ln4$

36) $ln(x^2 - 2x + 1) + ln2 = ln8$

Answers of Worksheets

Rewriting Logarithms

1) $3^3 = 27$

2) $(\frac{1}{5})^2 = \frac{1}{25}$

3) $4^3 = 64$

4) $7^{-2} = \frac{1}{49}$

5) $(\frac{1}{8})^{-3} = 512$

6) $(\frac{2}{3})^4 = \frac{16}{81}$

7) $16^{\frac{1}{2}} = 4$

8) $64^{-\frac{1}{2}} = \frac{1}{8}$

9) $5^5 = 3125$

10) $6^3 = 216$

11) $(\frac{1}{10})^{-4} = 10000$

12) $(\frac{1}{7})^{-3} = 343$

13) $2^{10} = 1024$

14) $3^{-4} = \frac{1}{81}$

15) $(\frac{2}{5})^{\frac{1}{2}} = \sqrt{\frac{2}{5}}$

16) $(\frac{2}{10})^{-4} = 625$

17) $4^{-5} = \frac{1}{1024}$

18) $(\frac{7}{10})^{-3} = \frac{1000}{343}$

19) $(\frac{3}{8})^3 = \frac{27}{512}$

20) $(\frac{3}{5})^{-2} = \frac{25}{9}$

21) $log_{\frac{1}{5}} \frac{1}{\sqrt{5}} = \frac{1}{2}$

22) $log_{\frac{1}{3}} \frac{1}{9} = 3$

23) $log_{\frac{4}{7}} \frac{49}{16} = -2$

24) $log_7 2401 = 4$

25) $log_{\frac{2}{5}} \frac{125}{8} = -3$

26) $log_{\frac{5}{4}} \frac{\sqrt{5}}{2} = \frac{1}{2}$

27) $log_{12} 144 = 2$

28) $log_{\frac{9}{8}} \frac{729}{512} = 3$

29) $log_6 \frac{1}{216} = -3$

30) $log_{100} 10 = \frac{1}{2}$

31) $log_{125} \frac{1}{5} = -\frac{1}{3}$

32) $log_6 \frac{1}{7776} = -5$

33) $log_{\frac{25}{9}} \frac{3}{5} = -\frac{1}{2}$

34) $log_{\frac{7}{11}} \frac{121}{49} = -2$

Evaluating Logarithms

1) 3

2) -5

3) $-\frac{1}{2}$

4) -4

5) $-\frac{1}{2}$

6) $-\frac{1}{4}$

7) -5

8) $-\frac{1}{3}$

9) 3

10) -3

11) -2

12) -2

13) $-\frac{1}{2}$

14) $\frac{3}{2}$

15) $\frac{2}{5}$

16) 0

17) -5

18) $-\frac{7}{2}$

19) $(0, -3)$

20) $(\frac{3}{2}, 0)$

21) $(3, 5)$

22) $(2, -11)$

23) $(10, 11)$

24) $(5, 7)$

25) $(4, 0)$

Properties of Logarithms

1) $log\ 25 + log\ 18$

2) $log\ 30 + log\ 12$

3) $log\ 9 + log\ 8$

4) $log\ 10 - log\ 27$

5) $log\ 6 - log\ 15$

6) $-3\ log\ 41 + 3\ log\ 29$

7) $-2log\ 11 + 2\ log\ 6$

8) $-2log\ 16 + 2\ log\ 9$

9) $-6\ log\ 6 + 2log\ 13$

10) $5\ log\ 3x - 10\ log\ y$

11) $2log\ x + \frac{1}{2}log\ y + 5\ log\ z$

12) $4(\ log\ a.\ log\ b) - log\ c$

13) $log\ 3q - 3\ log\ r$

14) $log\ \frac{15}{2^2}$

15) $log(7^3\ .\ 9)$

16) $log\ \frac{7^3}{8^2}$

17) $log\ \frac{15^5}{6^3}$

18) $log\ \frac{14^5}{14^2}$

19) $log\ \frac{11^{11}}{7^3}$

20) $log\ \frac{13}{4^4}$

21) $log\ \frac{5^7}{16^4}$

22) $log\ (2^{17}5^6)$

23) $log\ _7\ (7x \times (9y)^7)$

24) $log\ _5\ \frac{(3k)^4}{(4g)^3}$

25) $log\ _8\ \frac{6r}{(2s)^2}$

26) $log\ _3((2u)^3 \times (4v)^3)$

27) $log\ _2\ \frac{(4w)^6}{u^{11}}$

Natural Logarithms

1) $x = ln\ 10$

2) $x = ln\ 12$

3) $x = ln\ 13$

4) $x = e^{-3}$

5) $x = e^{e^3}$

6) $x = ln\ 14$

7) $x = \frac{e^9-6}{3}$

8) $x = e^3 - 2$

9) $x = \frac{e^8 +2}{4}$

10) $x = \frac{e^{\frac{1}{4}}}{2}$

11) $x = \frac{e^{2e^3}}{5}$

12) $x = 40$

13) $x = 972$

14) 0

15) -5

16) 2

17) $ln3 - 2$

18) -2

19) -3

20) 8

21) $\frac{1}{25}$

22) 72

23) $\frac{2}{3}$

24) 80

25) $\frac{e^2}{4}$

26) -2

27) 4

28) 64

29) $\frac{2}{3e}$

30) 0

31) 15

32) $2ln2$

33) $\frac{27}{e^4}$

34) $\frac{3}{e}$

35) 0

Exponential Equations and Logarithms

1) 2

2) 2

3) 2

4) 1

5) $\frac{1}{4}$

6) 3

7) 2

8) 2.4

9) $\frac{1}{2}$

10) 3

11) 0

12) -2

13) $\frac{5}{4}$

14) 2

15) -3

16) $\frac{1}{4}$

17) 1

18) $\frac{3}{5}$

19) $-\frac{4}{5}$

20) 1
21) -32
22) 2
23) -2

24) 2
25) 5
26) 28
27) 25

28) 285
29) $6082.8
30) $9165.12

Solving Logarithmic Equations

1) $\{\frac{9}{2}\}$
2) $\{\frac{1}{12}\}$
3) $\{\frac{7}{5}\}$
4) $\{\frac{5}{2}\}$
5) $\{\frac{729}{2}\}$
6) $\{\frac{1}{12}\}$
7) $\{0\}$
8) $\{-\frac{5}{7}\}$
9) $\{-4,2\}$
10) $\{-\frac{30}{77}\}$
11) $\{3,-4\}$
12) $\{+2,-2\}$
13) 1
14) $\{1,-1\}$
15) $\{2\}$
16) $\{-2,1\}$
17) $\{+\frac{1}{4},-\frac{1}{4}\}$
18) $\{-\frac{1}{6}\}$

19) $e-1$
20) $\{\frac{1}{46}\}$
21) $\{-1\}$
22) $\{4\}$
23) $\{2,-3\}$
24) $\{-\frac{3}{10}\}$
25) $\{3,-1\}$
26) $\{13\}$
27) $\{-\frac{1}{2}\}$
28) $\{0,10\}$
29) $\{4,-1\}$
30) $\{9\}$
31) $\{\frac{1}{2}\}$
32) $\{1,-1\}$
33) $\{-1\}$
34) $\{\frac{1}{8}\}$
35) $\{\frac{5}{2}\}$
36) $\{3,-1\}$

CLEP College Mathematics Test Review

College-Level Examination Program (CLEP) is a series of 33 standardized tests that measures your knowledge of certain subjects. You can earn college credit at thousands of colleges and universities by earning a satisfactory score on a computer- based CLEP exam.

The CLEP College Mathematics measures your knowledge of math topics generally taught in a college course for non-mathematics majors. It contains approximately 60 multiple choice questions to be answered in 90 minutes. Some of these questions are pretest questions that will not be scored. These 60 questions cover: sets, logic, the real number system, functions and graphing, probability and statistics, and additional topics from algebra and geometry. A scientific calculator is available to students during the entire testing time.

The CLEP College mathematics exam score ranges from 20 to 80 converting to A, B, C, or D based on this score. The letter grade is applied to your college course equivalent.

In this section, there are two complete CLEP College Mathematics Tests. Take these tests to see what score you'll be able to receive on a real CLEP College Mathematics test.

Good luck!

CLEP College Mathematics Practice Tests

Time to Test

Time to refine your skill with a practice examination

Take practice CLEP College Mathematics Tests to simulate the test day experience. After you've finished, score your tests using the answer keys.

Before You Start

- You'll need a pencil, a calculator and a timer to take the test.

- For each question, there are four possible answers. Choose which one is best.

- It's okay to guess. There is no penalty for wrong answers.

- Use the answer sheet provided to record your answers.

- After you've finished the test, review the answer key to see where you went wrong.

Good Luck!

CLEP College Mathematics Practice Tests Answer Sheets

CLEP College Mathematics Practice Test 1			
1 Ⓐ Ⓑ Ⓒ Ⓓ	16 Ⓐ Ⓑ Ⓒ Ⓓ	31 Ⓐ Ⓑ Ⓒ Ⓓ	46 Ⓐ Ⓑ Ⓒ Ⓓ
2 Ⓐ Ⓑ Ⓒ Ⓓ	17 Ⓐ Ⓑ Ⓒ Ⓓ	32 Ⓐ Ⓑ Ⓒ Ⓓ	47 Ⓐ Ⓑ Ⓒ Ⓓ
3 Ⓐ Ⓑ Ⓒ Ⓓ	18 Ⓐ Ⓑ Ⓒ Ⓓ	33 Ⓐ Ⓑ Ⓒ Ⓓ	48 Ⓐ Ⓑ Ⓒ Ⓓ
4 Ⓐ Ⓑ Ⓒ Ⓓ	19 Ⓐ Ⓑ Ⓒ Ⓓ	34 Ⓐ Ⓑ Ⓒ Ⓓ	39 Ⓐ Ⓑ Ⓒ Ⓓ
5 Ⓐ Ⓑ Ⓒ Ⓓ	20 Ⓐ Ⓑ Ⓒ Ⓓ	35 Ⓐ Ⓑ Ⓒ Ⓓ	50 Ⓐ Ⓑ Ⓒ Ⓓ
6 Ⓐ Ⓑ Ⓒ Ⓓ	21 Ⓐ Ⓑ Ⓒ Ⓓ	36 Ⓐ Ⓑ Ⓒ Ⓓ	51 Ⓐ Ⓑ Ⓒ Ⓓ
7 Ⓐ Ⓑ Ⓒ Ⓓ	22 Ⓐ Ⓑ Ⓒ Ⓓ	37 Ⓐ Ⓑ Ⓒ Ⓓ	52 Ⓐ Ⓑ Ⓒ Ⓓ
8 Ⓐ Ⓑ Ⓒ Ⓓ	23 Ⓐ Ⓑ Ⓒ Ⓓ	38 Ⓐ Ⓑ Ⓒ Ⓓ	53 Ⓐ Ⓑ Ⓒ Ⓓ
9 Ⓐ Ⓑ Ⓒ Ⓓ	24 Ⓐ Ⓑ Ⓒ Ⓓ	39 Ⓐ Ⓑ Ⓒ Ⓓ	54 Ⓐ Ⓑ Ⓒ Ⓓ
10 Ⓐ Ⓑ Ⓒ Ⓓ	25 Ⓐ Ⓑ Ⓒ Ⓓ	40 Ⓐ Ⓑ Ⓒ Ⓓ	55 Ⓐ Ⓑ Ⓒ Ⓓ
11 Ⓐ Ⓑ Ⓒ Ⓓ	26 Ⓐ Ⓑ Ⓒ Ⓓ	41 Ⓐ Ⓑ Ⓒ Ⓓ	56 Ⓐ Ⓑ Ⓒ Ⓓ
12 Ⓐ Ⓑ Ⓒ Ⓓ	27 Ⓐ Ⓑ Ⓒ Ⓓ	42 Ⓐ Ⓑ Ⓒ Ⓓ	57 Ⓐ Ⓑ Ⓒ Ⓓ
13 Ⓐ Ⓑ Ⓒ Ⓓ	28 Ⓐ Ⓑ Ⓒ Ⓓ	43 Ⓐ Ⓑ Ⓒ Ⓓ	58 Ⓐ Ⓑ Ⓒ Ⓓ
14 Ⓐ Ⓑ Ⓒ Ⓓ	29 Ⓐ Ⓑ Ⓒ Ⓓ	44 Ⓐ Ⓑ Ⓒ Ⓓ	59 Ⓐ Ⓑ Ⓒ Ⓓ
15 Ⓐ Ⓑ Ⓒ Ⓓ	30 Ⓐ Ⓑ Ⓒ Ⓓ	45 Ⓐ Ⓑ Ⓒ Ⓓ	60 Ⓐ Ⓑ Ⓒ Ⓓ

CLEP College Mathematics Practice Test 2

1 A B C D	16 A B C D	31 A B C D	46 A B C D	
2 A B C D	17 A B C D	32 A B C D	47 A B C D	
3 A B C D	18 A B C D	33 A B C D	48 A B C D	
4 A B C D	19 A B C D	34 A B C D	39 A B C D	
5 A B C D	20 A B C D	35 A B C D	50 A B C D	
6 A B C D	21 A B C D	36 A B C D	51 A B C D	
7 A B C D	22 A B C D	37 A B C D	52 A B C D	
8 A B C D	23 A B C D	38 A B C D	53 A B C D	
9 A B C D	24 A B C D	39 A B C D	54 A B C D	
10 A B C D	25 A B C D	40 A B C D	55 A B C D	
11 A B C D	26 A B C D	41 A B C D	56 A B C D	
12 A B C D	27 A B C D	42 A B C D	57 A B C D	
13 A B C D	28 A B C D	43 A B C D	58 A B C D	
14 A B C D	29 A B C D	44 A B C D	59 A B C D	
15 A B C D	30 A B C D	45 A B C D	60 A B C D	

CLEP College Mathematics

Practice Test 1

60 questions

Total time for this section: 90 Minutes

You can use a scientific calculator on this test.

1) What is the equation of the graph?

A. $x^2 + 6x + 5$

B. $x^2 + 2x + 4$

C. $2x^2 - 4x + 4$

D. $2x^2 + 4x + 2$

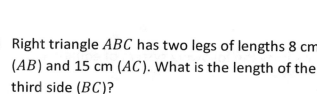

2) Right triangle ABC has two legs of lengths 8 cm (AB) and 15 cm (AC). What is the length of the third side (BC)?

A. 11 cm

B. 13 cm

C. 15 cm

D. 17 cm

3) If $A = \{1, 5, 10, 15, 20\}$, $B = \{3, 6, 9, 12\}$, and $C = \{2, 4, 6, 8, 10, 12, 14\}$, then which of the following set is $(A \cup B) \cap C$?

A. $\{1, 3, 5, 6, 9, 10, 12, 15, 20\}$

B. $\{2, 3, 4, 6, 8, 9, 10, 12, 14\}$

C. $\{10, 15, 20\}$

D. $\{6, 10, 12\}$

4) If $6n + 3 \geq 2$, what is the least possible value of $6n - 4$?

A. -2

B. -3

C. -4

D. -5

5) A ladder leans against a wall forming a 60° angle between the ground and the ladder. If the bottom of the ladder is 35 feet away from the wall, how long is the ladder?

A. 23 feet

B. 35 feet

C. 55 feet

D. 70 feet

6) If $A = \{1, 4, 7, 10, 13, 16, 19\}$ and $B = \{1, 4, 8, 12, 16, 20\}$, how many elements are in $A \cap B$?

A. 1

B. 3

C. 5

D. 7

7) What is the solution of the following inequality?

$$|x + 8| \leq 5$$

A. $x \geq -3 \cup x \leq -13$

B. $-13 \leq x \leq -3$

C. $x \geq -3$

D. $x \leq -13$

E. Set of real numbers

8) A bank is offering 5.5% simple interest on a savings account. If you deposit $12,000, how much interest will you earn in eight years?

A. $3,850

C. $5,280

B. $4,640

D. $,6230

9) The area of a circle is less than 81 π. Which of the following can be the circumference of the circle?

A. 16 π

C. 21 π

B. 18 π

D. 25 π

10) Which of the following values for x and y satisfy the following system of equations?
$$\begin{cases} 2x + 4y = -10 \\ 6x + 3y = 6 \end{cases}$$

A. $x = -3, y = -4$
B. $x = -3, y = 4$
C. $x = 3, y = 4$
D. $x = 3, y = -4$

11) If 80% of A is 16% of B, then B is what percent of A?

A. 0.5%

C. 50%

B. 5%

D. 500%

12) The price of a car was $30,000 in 2015, $24,000 in 2016 and $19,200 in 2017. What is the rate of depreciation of the price of car per year?

A.15%

C.25%

B. 20%

D. 30%

13) The width of a box is one fourth of its length. The height of the box is one second of its width. If the length of the box is 48 cm, what is the volume of the box?

A. 2,563 cm^3

C. 3,456 cm^3

B. 2,874 cm^3

D. 3,982 cm^3

14) How many possible outfit combinations come from five shirts, four slacks, and three ties?

A. 32

C. 54

B. 48

D. 60

15) If 60% of a class are girls, and 22% of girls play tennis, what percent of the class play tennis?

A. 8.8%

C. 18.3%

B. 13.2%

D. 23.4%

16) A $64 shirt now selling for $48 is discounted by what percent?
   A. 20%   C. 30%

   B. 25%   D. 35%

17) 48 is What percent of 24?
   A. 50%   C. 200%

   B. 150%   D. 250%

18) If the area of trapezoid is 120 cm, what is the perimeter of the trapezoid?
   A. 36 cm
   B. 48 cm
   C. 56 cm
   D. 64 cm

19) In four successive hours, a car travels 55 km, 68 km, 48 km, and 72 km. In the next four hours, it travels with an average speed of 64 km per hour. Find the total distance the car traveled in 8 hours.

   A. 395 km   C. 499 km

   B. 483 km   D. 517 km

20) How long does a 468–miles trip take moving at 72 miles per hour (mph)?
   A. 6 hours

   B. 6 hours and 25 minutes

   C. 6 hours and 30 minutes

   D. 6 hours and 40 minutes

21) In the xy-plane, the point (5, -2) and (3, 4) are on line A. Which of the following points could also be on line A? (Select one or more answer choices)
   A. $(-1, 1)$ C. $(3, 2)$

   B. $(2, 3)$ D. $(4, 1)$

22) One third of 27 is equal to $\frac{3}{4}$ of what number?
   A. 10   C. 15

   B. 12   D. 18

23) The marked price of a computer is D dollar. Its price decreased by 15% in January and later increased by 20 % in February. What is the final price of the computer in D dollar?

A. 0.80 D

C. 0.95 D

B. 0.85 D

D. 1.02 D

24) A line in the xy-plane passes through origin and has a slope of $\frac{1}{4}$. Which of the following points lies on the line?

A. (2, 1)

C. (4, 1)

B. (3, -1)

D. (4, 2)

25) How many tiles of 11 cm² is needed to cover a floor of dimension 8 cm by 22 cm?

A. 9

C. 16

B. 14

D. 19

26) Which of the following lists shows the fractions in order from least to greatest?

$$\frac{7}{9}, \frac{3}{5}, \frac{4}{7}, \frac{5}{13}$$

A. $\frac{3}{5}, \frac{4}{7}, \frac{7}{9}, \frac{5}{13}$

C. $\frac{4}{7}, \frac{3}{5}, \frac{5}{13}, \frac{7}{9}$

B. $\frac{4}{7}, \frac{5}{13}, \frac{3}{5}, \frac{7}{9}$

D. $\frac{5}{13}, \frac{4}{7}, \frac{3}{5}, \frac{7}{9}$

27) A boat sails 12 miles south and then 16 miles east. How far is the boat from its start point?

A. 14 miles

C. 20 miles

B. 18 miles

D. 24 miles

28) The ratio of boys and girls in a class is 5:7. If there are 60 students in the class, how many more boys should be enrolled to make the ratio 1:1?

A. 10

C. 16

B. 14

D. 18

29) Sophia purchased a sofa for $535.44. The sofa is regularly priced at $582. What was the percent discount Sophia received on the sofa?

A. 8%

C. 15%

B. 12%

D. 20%

30) The score of Emma was twice that of Ava and the score of Mia was half as that of Ava. If the score of Mia was 30, what is the score of Emma?

A. 30

C. 75

B. 55

D. 120

31) A bag contains 19 balls: two green, six black, eight blue, a brown, a red and one white. If 18 balls are removed from the bag at random, what is the probability that a red ball has been removed?

A. $\frac{13}{19}$

C. $\frac{17}{19}$

B. $\frac{14}{19}$

D. $\frac{18}{19}$

32) The average of five consecutive numbers is 45. What is the smallest number?

A. 35

C. 40

B. 39

D. 43

33) Which of the following could be the product of two consecutive prime numbers?

A. 2

C. 14

B. 10

D. 15

34) In the xy-plane, the point (4, 2) and (6, 8) are on line A. Which of the following equations of lines is parallel to line A?

A. $y = 2x - 5$

C. $y = 3x - 1$

B. $y = \frac{1}{2}x + 3$

D. $y = \frac{1}{3}x + 3$

35) A chemical solution contains 15% alcohol. If there is 36 ml of alcohol, what is the volume of the solution?

A. 210 ml

C. 290 ml

B. 240 ml

D. 340 ml

36) The average weight of 24 girls in a class is 68 kg and the average weight of 16 boys in the same class is 75 kg. What is the average weight of all the 40 students in that class?

A. 69.5

C. 72.8

B. 70.8

D. 73.2

37) Which of the following numbers is NOT a solution of the inequality $3x - 6 \geq 2x - 8$?

A. -3

C. -1

B. -2

D. 0

38) If the following equations are true, what is the value of x?

$$a = \sqrt{5}$$
$$6a = \sqrt{3x}$$

A. 15

C. 45

B. 20

D. 60

39) The surface area of a cylinder is $130\pi\ cm^2$. If its height is 8 cm, what is the radius of the cylinder?
   A. 5 cm
   B. 7 cm
   C. 13 cm
   D. 15 cm

40) In 1875, the average worker's income increased $1,200 per year starting from $14,400 annual salary. Which equation represents income greater than average? (I = income, x = number of years after 1875)
   A. $I > 1200\ x + 14400$
   B. $I > -1200\ x + 14400$
   C. $I < -1200\ x + 14400$
   D. $I < 1200\ x - 14400$

41) If the function $g(x)$ has four distinct zeros, which of the following could represent the graph of $g(x)$?

A.
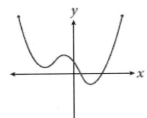

B.
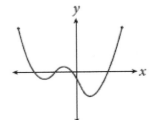

C.
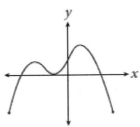

D.
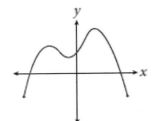

42) If 30% of x equal to 45% of 24, then what is the value of $(x - 6)^2$?
   A. 625
   B. 793
   C. 842
   D. 900

43) A rope weighs 600 grams per meter of length. What is the weight in kilograms of 14.6 meters of this rope? (1 kilograms = 1000 grams)
   A. 0.0876
   B. 0.876
   C. 8.76
   D. 87.60

44) If $y = 5a^2b - 3ab^3$, what is y when a = 2 and b = -1?
   A. -16
   B. -14
   C. 14
   D. 16

45) A boat sails 36 miles south and then 77 miles east. How far is the boat from its start point?
A. 65 miles
B. 79 miles
C. 85 miles
D. 91 miles

46) For what real value of x is the equation below true?
$$x^3 - 7x^2 + 4x - 28 = 0$$
A. 3
B. 5
C. 7
D. 9

47) If $f(x) = 7^x$ and $g(x) = log_7 x$, which of the following expressions is equal to $f(7g(p))$?
A. $7P$
B. 7^p
C. p^7
D. p^{-7}

48) The cost of using a car is $0.98 per minutes. Which of the following equations represents the total cost c, in dollars, for h hours of using the car?
A. $c = \dfrac{60h}{0.98}$
B. $c = \dfrac{0.98}{60h}$
C. $c = 0.98\,(60h)$
D. $c = 60h + 0.98$

49) Mary's average score after 3 tests is 90. What score on the 4th test would bring Mary's average up to exactly 92?
A. 95
B. 96
C. 97
D. 98

50) The equation $x^2 = 24 - 5x$ has how many distinct real solutions?
A. 0
B. 1
C. 2
D. 3

51) In the following equation when z is divided by 2, what is the effect on x?
$$x = \frac{8y + \dfrac{r}{r+1}}{\dfrac{6}{z}}$$
A. x is divided by 2
B. x is divided by 4
C. x does not change
D. x is multiplied by 2

52) If $f(x) = x^3 - 4x^2 + 3x - 6$ and $g(x) = 3$, what is the value of $f(g(x))$?
A. -8
B. -6
C. 6
D. 8

53) a is b% of what number?

A. $\dfrac{100a}{b}$

B. $\dfrac{100b}{a}$

C. $\dfrac{a}{100b}$

D. $\dfrac{b}{100a}$

54) In the xy −plane, the line determined by the points $(7, m)$ and $(m, 14)$ passes through the origin. Which of the following could be the value of m?

A. $\sqrt{2}$

B. $\sqrt{7}$

C. $2\sqrt{7}$

D. $7\sqrt{2}$

55) A function $g(5) = 7$ and $g(8) = 6$. A function $f(7) = 3$ and $f(6) = 4$. What is the value of $f(g(8))$?

A. 3

B. 4

C. 6

D. 7

56) Which of the following points lies on the line $3x - 2y = 12$?

A. (-1, 2)

B. (1, 3)

C. (2, -3)

D. (2, 2)

57) Point A lies on the line with equation $3y + 3 = 6(x - 4)$. If the x −coordinate of A is 7, what is the y −coordinate of A?

A. 3

B. 5

C. 7

D. 9

58) If $|a| < 1$, then which of the following is true? $(b > 0)$?

       I.$- b < ba < b$

       II.$-a < a^2 < a \quad if \ a < 0$

       III.$-5 < 4a - 3 < 7$

A. I only

B. III only

C. I and III only

D. I, II and III

$$\frac{c - d}{c} = a$$

59) In the equation above, if c is negative and d is positive, which of the following must be true?

A. $a < 1$

B. $a = 0$

C. $a > 1$

D. $a < -1$

60) If $f(x) = 2x^2 - 5x + 1$ and $g(x) = -3x^2 - 6x + 4$, then find $(f - g)(x)$?

A. $-x^2 + x - 1$

B. $x^2 - x + 1$

C. $-5x^2 - x + 3$

D. $5x^2 + x - 3$

IF YOU FINISH BEFORE TIME IS CALLED, YOU MAY CHECK YOUR WORK ON THIS TEST ONLY.

STOP

CLEP College Mathematics

Practice Test 2

60 questions

Total time for this section: 90 Minutes

You can use a scientific calculator on this test.

1) Mr. Carlos family are choosing a menu for their reception. They have 4 choices of appetizers, 2 choices of entrees, 3 choices of cake. How many different menu combinations are possible for them to choose?

A. 9

B. 12

C. 16

D. 24

2) Simplify the expression.
$$\left(8x^4 - 3x^3 + 6x^2\right) - \left(5x^4 + 7x^2 - 5x\right)$$

A. $3x^4 + 4x^3 - 13x^2$

B. $3x^4 - 3x^3 - x^2 + 5x$

C. $4x^3 + x^3 - x^2 - 5x$

D. $3x^4 - x^2 + 5x$

3) In two successive years, the population of a town is increased by 12% and 10%. What percent of the population is increased after two years?

A. 20%

B. 23%

C. 28%

D. 32%

4) Which of the following graphs represents the compound inequality $1 \le 2x - 5 < 11$?

A.

B.

C.
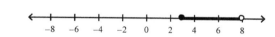

D.

5) What is the volume of a box with the following dimensions?
Hight = 5 cm   Width = 4 cm   Length = 8 cm

A. 17 cm^3

B. 32 cm^3

C. 120 cm^3

D. 160 cm^3

6) If $3n - 7 \ge 1$, what is the least possible value of $3n + 2$?

A. 8

B. 9

C. 10

D. 11

7) Two dice are thrown simultaneously, what is the probability of getting a sum of 3 or 5?

A. $\frac{1}{4}$

C. $\frac{1}{9}$

B. $\frac{1}{6}$

D. $\frac{1}{12}$

8) Last week 36,000 fans attended a football match. This week four times as many bought tickets, but one sixth of them cancelled their tickets. How many are attending this week?

A. 85,000

C. 120,000

B. 92,000

D. 144,000

9) What is the perimeter of a square in centimeters that has an area of 1,024 cm²?

A. 96

C. 144

B. 128

D. 169

10) Which of the following points lies on the line $2x - y = 5$?

A. $(-1, 4)$

C. $(3, 1)$

B. $(2, -3)$

D. $(4, 2)$

11) The perimeter of a rectangular yard is 70 meters. What is its length if its width is one sixth its length?

A. 18 meters

C. 30 meters

B. 24 meters

D. 42 meters

12) Which of the following shows the numbers in descending order?
$$\frac{7}{9}, \frac{3}{4}, 85\%, \frac{2}{5}$$

A. $85\%, \frac{2}{5}, \frac{3}{4}, \frac{7}{9}$

C. $\frac{7}{9}, 85\%, \frac{3}{4}, \frac{2}{5}$

B. $\frac{2}{5}, \frac{3}{4}, \frac{7}{9}, 85\%$

D. $\frac{2}{5}, 85\%, \frac{7}{9}, \frac{3}{4}$

13) The mean of 25 test scores was calculated as 94. But, it turned out that one of the scores was misread as 86 but it was 68. What is the correct mean of the test scores?

A. 92

C. 93

B. 92.25

D. 93.28

14) In a stadium the ratio of home fans to visiting fans in a crowd is 5:8. Which of the following could be the total number of fans in the stadium?

A. 9,862

C. 23,577

B. 11,480

D. 32,227

15) A card is drawn at random from a standard 52–card deck, what is the probability that the card is of Hearts? (The deck includes 13 of each suit clubs, diamonds, hearts, and spades)

A. $\dfrac{1}{3}$

B. $\dfrac{1}{4}$

C. $\dfrac{1}{6}$

D. $\dfrac{1}{52}$

16) What is the area of a square whose diagonal is 6?

A. 12

B. 18

C. 24

D. 32

17) Anita's trick–or–treat bag contains 15 pieces of chocolate, 16 suckers, 22 pieces of gum, 15 pieces of licorice. If she randomly pulls a piece of candy from her bag, what is the probability of her pulling out a piece of sucker?

A. $\dfrac{4}{15}$

B. $\dfrac{7}{15}$

C. $\dfrac{4}{17}$

D. $\dfrac{6}{17}$

18) The average of 8 numbers is 18. The average of 6 of those numbers is 16. What is the average of the other two numbers?

A. 24

B. 28

C. 32

D. 36

19) 6. What is the value of x in the following system of equations?

$$x + y = 5$$
$$2x + y = 7$$

A. -3

B. -2

C. 2

D. 3

20) The perimeter of the trapezoid below is 50 cm. What is its area?

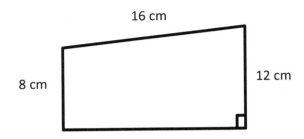

16 cm

8 cm

12 cm

A. 98 cm^2

C. 140 cm^2

B. 115 cm^2

D. 165 cm^2

21) If 120 % of a number is 84, then what is the 85 % of that number?

A. 48.5

C. 59.5

B. 52.3

D. 62.4

22) If $f(x) = 5x^2 - 2x$ and $g(x) = 6x - 4$, then find $(\frac{f}{g})(x)$.

A. $\dfrac{5x^2 - 2x}{6x - 4}$

C. $\dfrac{5x - 2}{6x}$

B. $\dfrac{6x - 4}{5x^2 - 2x}$

D. $\dfrac{6x}{5x + 2}$

23) A swimming pool holds 4,410 cubic feet of water. The swimming pool is 35 feet long and 14 feet wide. How deep is the swimming pool?

A. 9

C. 13

B. 11

D. 17

24) The square of a number is $\frac{49}{81}$. What is the cube of that number?

A. $\dfrac{7}{9}$

C. $\dfrac{343}{81}$

B. $\dfrac{49}{729}$

D. $\dfrac{343}{729}$

25) The length of a rectangle is 4 meters greater than 2 times its width. The perimeter of the rectangle is 32 meters. What is the area of the rectangle in meters?

A. 36

C. 48

B. 42

D. 56

26) Which of the following is equal to $b^{\frac{3}{4}}$?

A. $\sqrt{b^{\frac{3}{4}}}$

C. $\sqrt[4]{b^3}$

B. $b^{\frac{4}{3}}$

D. $\sqrt[3]{b^4}$

27) Mr. Jones saves $3,200 out of his monthly family income of $96,000. What fractional part of his income does he save?

A. $\dfrac{1}{30}$

B. $\dfrac{7}{30}$

C. $\dfrac{1}{12}$

D. $\dfrac{7}{12}$

28) Jason needs an 85% average in his writing class to pass. On his first 5 exams, he earned scores of 92%, 83%, 75%, 89% and 76%. What is the minimum score Jason can earn on his 6th and final test to pass?

A. 95

B. 97

C. 99

D. 100

29) What is the value of x in the following equation?

$$\frac{3}{8}x + \frac{5}{24} = \frac{3}{4}$$

A. $\dfrac{5}{8}$

B. $\dfrac{8}{5}$

C. $\dfrac{9}{13}$

D. $\dfrac{13}{9}$

30) What is the surface area of the cylinder below?(h=12, D=8)

A. $64 \; \pi \; in^2$

B. $81 \; \pi \; in^2$

C. $112 \; \pi \; in^2$

D. $128 \; \pi \; in^2$

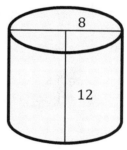

31) The average of six numbers is 28. If a sixth number that is greater than 49 is added, then, which of the following could be the new average? (Select one or more answer choices)

A. 22

B. 25

C. 26

D. 27

32) A bank is offering 4.5% simple interest on a savings account. If you deposit $15,000, how much interest will you earn in 6 years?

A. $3840

B. $4050

C. $4850

D. $5220

33) Right triangle ABC has two legs of lengths 5 cm (AB) and 12 cm (AC). What is the length of the third side (BC)?

A. 7 cm   C. 13 cm

B. 9 cm   D. 15 cm

34) What is the equivalent temperature of 122°F in Celsius?

$$C = \frac{5}{9}(F - 32)$$

A. 39   C. 50

B. 46   D. 57

35) If 60% of a number is 3, what is the number?

A. 4   C. 7

B. 5   D. 8

36) The circle graph below shows all Mr. Green's expenses for last month. If he spent $8400 on his car, how much did he spend for his bills?

A. $462.4

B. $495.2

C. $525.3

D. $537.6

Mr. Green's monthly expenses

37) Jason is 12 miles ahead of Joe running at 6.5 miles per hour and Joe is running at the speed of 8 miles per hour. How long does it take Joe to catch Jason?

A. 7 hours   C. 8 hours

B. 7.5 hours   D. 8.5 hours

38) 72 students took an exam and 18 of them failed. What percent of the students passed the exam?

A. 60%   C. 70%

B. 65%   D. 75%

39) What is the median of these numbers? 28, 32, 79, 57, 13, 6, 61

A. 6   C. 32

B. 13   D. 79

40) Which of the following is the equation of a quadratic graph with a vertex $(2, -2)$?
   A. $y = 2x^2 - 2$
   B. $y = -2x^2 + 2$
   C. $y = x^2 + 2x - 2$
   D. $y = 4(x - 2)^2 + 2$

x	1	2	3
$g(x)$	1	5	7

41) The table above shows some values of linear function $g(x)$. Which of the following defines $g(x)$?
   A. $g(x) = x + 1$
   B. $g(x) = 2x + 1$
   C. $g(x) = 2x - 1$
   D. $g(x) = x^2 + 1$

42) Which of the following expressions is equal to $\sqrt{\frac{x^2}{8} + \frac{x^2}{16}}$?
   A. x
   B. $\frac{3}{4}x$
   C. $\frac{\sqrt{3}}{4}x$
   D. $\frac{x\sqrt{x}}{4}$

43) What is the $y-$intercept of the line with the equation $4x - 3y = 18$?
   A. -8
   B. -6
   C. 6
   D. 8

44) If $6a - 9 = 33$ what is the value of $3a$?
   A. 7
   B. 12
   C. 16
   D. 21

45) If $x \neq 0$ and $x = x^{-6}$, what is the value of x?
   A. -2
   B. 1
   C. 2
   D. 3

46) Which of the following is equal to expression $\frac{3}{2x} - \frac{5x-8}{6x^2}$?
   A. $\frac{8x+4}{2x^2}$
   B. $\frac{4x+8}{x^2}$
   C. $\frac{2x-4}{3x^2}$
   D. $\frac{2x+4}{3x^2}$

47) Simplify $3x^2y^2(4xy^3)^2 =$
   A. $12x^4y^6$
   B. $12x^4y^8$
   C. $48x^4y^6$
   D. $48x^4y^8$

48) What is the average of $3x - 5, 4x + 2$ and $5x + 6$?
   A. $2x - 2$
   B. $2x + 5$
   C. $4x - 3$
   D. $4x + 1$

49) What is the slope of a line that is perpendicular to the line
$$3x - 6y = 15?$$
A. $\dfrac{1}{2}$

B. $\dfrac{2}{3}$

C. -2

D. 2

50) If the ratio of $7a$ to $3b$ is $\dfrac{1}{12}$, what is the ratio of a to b?

A. $\dfrac{1}{15}$

B. $\dfrac{4}{15}$

C. $\dfrac{1}{28}$

D. $\dfrac{3}{28}$

51) What is the difference in area between a 8 cm by 6 cm rectangle and a circle with diameter of 12 cm? ($\pi = 3$)
A. 42
B. 48
C. 54
D. 60

52) If $f(x)=x^3 + 2x^2 + 7x$ and $g(x)= 2x$, what is the value of $f(g(x))$?
A. $8x^3 - 8x^2 + 14x$
B. $8x^3 + 8x^2 - 12x$
C. $12x^3 - 9x^2 - 14x$
D. $-12x^3 + 9x^2 + 12x$

53) What is the value of x in the following equation?
$$4^x = 1{,}024$$
A. 4
B. 5
C. 6
D. 7

54) A cruise line ship left Port A and traveled 20 miles due west and then 21 miles due north. At this point, what is the shortest distance from the cruise to port A?
A. 29 miles
B. 32 miles
C. 39 miles
D. 43 miles

55) The length of a rectangle is 6 meters greater than 3 times its width. The perimeter of the rectangle is 44 meters. What is the area of the rectangle?
A. 36 m^2
B. 48 m^2
C. 64 m^2
D. 72 m^2

56) Tickets to a movie cost $12 for adults and $8 for students. A group of 15 friends purchased tickets for $140. How many student tickets did they buy?
A. 5
B. 8
C. 10
D. 12

57) In a coordinate plane, triangle *ABC* has coordinates: (3, -2), (5, 1), and (-2, 3). If triangle *ABC* is reflected over the *y*-axis, what are the coordinates of the new image?
A. (-3, 2), (-5, -1), (2, -3)
B. (3, 2), (5, -1), (2, -3)
C. (-3, -2), (-5, 1), (2, 3)
D. (3, 2), (5, 1), (2, 3)

58) If $x = 3$, what is the value of y in the following equation?

$$4y = \frac{5x^2}{9} - 3$$

A. $\frac{3}{4}$

B. $\frac{1}{2}$

C. 3

D. 4

59) Sara orders a box of pen for $2 per box. A tax of 6.5% is added to the cost of the pens before a flat shipping fee of $8 closest out the transaction. Which of the following represents total cost of p boxes of pens in dollars?
A. $1.065(2p) + 8$
B. $8p + 2$
C. $1.065(8p) + 2$
D. $2p + 8$

60) A plant grows at a linear rate. After six weeks, the plant is 54 cm tall. Which of the following functions represents the relationship between the height (y) of the plant and number of weeks of growth (x)?
A. $y(x) = 54x + 9$
B. $y(x) = 9x + 54$
C. $y(x) = 54x$
D. $y(x) = 9x$

IF YOU FINISH BEFORE TIME IS CALLED, YOU MAY CHECK YOUR WORK ON THIS TEST ONLY.   STOP

CLEP College Mathematics Practice Tests Answers and Explanations

Now, it's time to review your results to see where you went wrong and what areas you need to improve!

CLEP College Mathematics Practice Test 1 Answer Key								CLEP College Mathematics Practice Test 2 Answer Key						
1	C	21	D	41	B		1	D	21	C	41	B		
2	D	22	B	42	D		2	B	22	A	42	C		
3	D	23	D	43	C		3	B	23	A	43	B		
4	D	24	C	44	B		4	C	24	D	44	D		
5	D	25	C	45	C		5	D	25	C	45	B		
6	B	26	D	46	C		6	B	26	C	46	D		
7	B	27	C	47	C		7	B	27	A	47	D		
8	C	28	A	48	C		8	C	28	A	48	D		
9	A	29	A	49	D		9	B	29	D	49	C		
10	D	30	D	50	C		10	C	30	D	50	C		
11	D	31	D	51	A		11	C	31	D	51	D		
12	B	32	D	52	B		12	B	32	B	52	A		
13	C	33	D	53	A		13	D	33	C	53	B		
14	D	34	C	54	D		14	D	34	C	54	A		
15	B	35	B	55	B		15	B	35	B	55	D		
16	B	36	B	56	C		16	B	36	D	56	C		
17	C	37	A	57	B		17	C	37	C	57	C		
18	B	38	D	58	A		18	A	38	D	58	B		
19	C	39	A	59	C		19	C	39	C	59	A		
20	C	40	A	60	D		20	C	40	D	60	D		

CLEP College Mathematics Practice Test 1

1) Choice C is correct

In order to figure out what the equation of the graph is, fist find the vertex. From the graph we can determine that the vertex is at (1,2). We can use vertex form to solve for the equation of this graph. Recall vertex form, $y = a(x - h)^2 + k$, where h is the x coordinate of the vertex, and k is the y coordinate of the vertex. Plugging in our values, you get $y = a(x - 1)^2 + 2$
To solve for a, we need to pick a point on the graph and plug it into the equation.
Let's pick $(-1, 10)$. $10 = a(-1 - 1)^2 + 2 \rightarrow 10 = a(-2)^2 + 2 \rightarrow 10 = 4a + 2$
$8 = 4a \rightarrow a = 2$ Now the equation is : $y = 2(x - 1)^2 + 2$
Let's expand this, $y = 2(x^2 - 2x + 1) + 2 \rightarrow y = 2x^2 - 4x + 2 + 2 \rightarrow y = 2x^2 - 4x + 4$
The equation in Choice C is the same.

2) Choice D is correct

Use Pythagorean Theorem: $a^2 + b^2 = c^2$. $\rightarrow 8^2 + 15^2 = c^2 \Rightarrow 64 + 225 = c^2 \Rightarrow 289 = c^2 \Rightarrow c = 17$

3) Choice D is correct

$A = \{1, 5, 10, 15, 20\}, B = \{3, 6, 9, 12\}, C = \{2, 4, 6, 8, 10, 12, 14\}$
The union of A and B is: $A \cup B = \{1, 3, 5, 6, 9, 10, 12, 15, 20\}$
The intersection of $(A \cup B)$ and C is: $(A \cup B) \cap C = \{6, 10, 12\}$

4) Choice D is correct

Subtracting 7 to each side of the inequality $6n + 3 \geq 2$ yields the inequality $6n - 4 \geq -5$. Therefore, the least possible value of $6n - 4$ is -5.

5) Choice D is correct

The relationship among all sides of special right triangle
$30° - 60° - 90°$ is provided in this triangle:
In this triangle, the opposite side of $30°$ angle is half of the hypotenuse.
Draw the shape of this question:
The ladder is the hypotenuse. Therefore, the ladder is 70 ft.

6) Choice B is correct

$A = \{1, 4, 7, 10, 13, 16, 19\}, B = \{1, 4, 8, 12, 16, 20\}$
The intersection of A and B is: $A \cap B = \{1, 4, 16\}$. There are 3 elements in $A \cap B$.

7) Choice B is correct

$|x + 8| \leq 5 \rightarrow -5 \leq x + 8 \leq 5 \rightarrow -5 - 8 \leq x + 8 - 8 \leq 5 - 8 \rightarrow -13 \leq x \leq -3$

8) Choice C is correct

Use simple interest formula: $I = prt$ $(I = interest, \ p = principal, \ r = rate, \ t = time)$

$$I = (12{,}000)(0.055)(8) = 5{,}280$$

9) Choice A is correct

Area of the circle is less than $81 \, \pi$. Use the formula of areas of circles.

$$Area = \pi r^2 \Rightarrow 81 \, \pi > \pi r^2 \Rightarrow 81 > r^2 \Rightarrow r < 9$$

Radius of the circle is less than 9. Let's put 9 for the radius. Now, use the circumference formula: $Circumference = 2\pi r = 2\pi(9) = 18\pi$, Since the radius of the circle is less than 9. Then, the circumference of the circle must be less than 18π. Only choice A is less than 18π.

10) Choice D is correct

$\begin{cases} 2x + 4y = -10 \\ 6x + 3y = 6 \end{cases} \rightarrow$ Multiply the top equation by -3 then,

$\begin{cases} -6x - 12y = 30 \\ 6x + 3y = 6 \end{cases} \rightarrow$ Add two equations. $-9y = 36 \rightarrow y = -4$, plug in the value of y into the first equation: $2x + 4y = -10 \rightarrow 2x + 4(-4) = -10$

Added 16 to both sides of the equation. $2x - 16 = -10 \rightarrow 2x - 16 + 16 = -10 + 16 = 6 \rightarrow 2x = 6 \rightarrow x = 3$

11) Choice D is correct

Write the equation and solve for B: $0.80\,A = 0.16\,B$, divide both sides by 0.16, then:

$0.80/0.16\,A = B$, therefore: $B = 5A$, and B is 5 times of A or it's 500% of A.

12) Choice B is correct

Use this formula: Percent of Change $\dfrac{\text{New Value} - \text{Old Value}}{Old\ Value} \times 100\%$

$\dfrac{24000 - 30000}{30000} \times 100\% = 20\%$ and $\dfrac{19200 - 24000}{24000} \times 100\% = 20\%$

13) Choice C is correct

If the length of the box is 48, then the width of the box is one fourth of it, 12, and the height of the box is 6 (one second of the width). The volume of the box is: $V = lwh = (48)(12)(6) = 3,456$

14) Choice D is correct

To find the number of possible outfit combinations, multiply number of options for each factor: $5 \times 4 \times 3 = 60$

15) Choice B is correct

The percent of girls playing tennis is: 60 % × 22 % = 0.60 × 0.22 = 0.132 = 13.2 %

16) Choice B is correct

Use the formula for Percent of Change $\dfrac{\text{New Value} - \text{Old Value}}{Old\ Value} \times 100\%$

$\dfrac{48 - 64}{64} \times 100\% = -25\%$ (Negative sign here means that the new price is less than old price).

17) Choice C is correct

Use percent formula: part $= \dfrac{\text{percent}}{100} \times$ whole

$48 = \frac{percent}{100} \times 24 \Rightarrow 48 = \frac{percent \times 24}{100}$, multiply both sides by 100.

$4800 = percent \times 24$, divide both sides by 24.

$200 = percent$

18) Choice B is correct

The area of the trapezoid is: $Area = \frac{1}{2}h(b_1 + b_2) = \frac{1}{2}(x)(18 + 12) = 120 \rightarrow 15x = 120 \rightarrow$
$x = 8$. $y = \sqrt{6^2 + 8^2} = \sqrt{36 + 64} = \sqrt{100} = 10$

The perimeter of the trapezoid is: $8 + 12 + 10 + 18 = 48$

19) Choice C is correct

Add the first 4 numbers. $55 + 68 + 48 + 72 = 243$

To find the distance traveled in the next 4 hours, multiply the average by number of hours.

Distance = Average × Rate = $64 \times 4 = 256$. Add both numbers. $243 + 256 = 499$

20) Choice C is correct

Use distance formula: Distance = Rate × time $\Rightarrow 468 = 72 \times T$, divide both sides by 72.
$\frac{468}{72} = T \rightarrow T = 6.5$ hours. Change hours to minutes for the decimal part. 0.5 hours =
$0.5 \times 60 = 30$ minutes.

21) Choice D is correct

The equation of a line is in the form of $y = mx + b$, where m is the slope of the line and b is
the $y - intercept$ of the line. Two points (5, -2) and (3, 4) are on line A. Therefore, the slope of
the line A is: $slope\ of\ line\ A = \frac{y_2 - y_1}{x_2 - x_1} = \frac{4-(-2)}{3-5} = \frac{6}{-2} = -3$

The slope of line A is -3. Thus, the formula of the line A is: $y = mx + b = -3x + b$, choose a
point and plug in the values of x and y in the equation to solve for b. Let's choose point (5, -2).
Then: $y = -3x + b \rightarrow -2 = -3(5) + b \rightarrow b = -2 + 15 = 13$

The equation of line A is: $y = -3x + 13$. Now, let's review the choices provided:

A. $(-1, 1)$ $y = -3x + 13 \rightarrow 1 = -3(-1) + 13 = 16$ This is not true.

B. $(2, 3)$ $y = -3x + 13 \rightarrow 3 = -3(2) + 13 = 7$ This is not true.

C. $(3, \ 2)$ $y = -3x + 13 \rightarrow 2 = -3(3) + 13 = 4$ This is not true.

D. $(4, 1)$ $y = -3x + 13 \rightarrow 1 = -3(4) + 13 = 1$ This is true!

22) Choice B is correct

Let x be the number. Write the equation and solve for x.

$\frac{1}{3} \times (27) = \frac{3}{4} \cdot x \Rightarrow \frac{1 \times 27}{3} = \frac{3x}{4}$, use cross multiplication to solve for x.

$4 \times 27 = 3x \times 3 \Rightarrow 108 = 9x \Rightarrow x = 12$

23) Choice D is correct
To find the discount, multiply the number by (100% − rate of discount).

Therefore, for the first discount we get: (D) (100% − 15%) = (D) (0.85) = 0.85 D

For increase of 20%: (0.85 D) (100% + 20%) = (0.85 D) (1.20) = 1.02 D = 102% of D

24) Choice C is correct
First, find the equation of the line. All lines through the origin are of the form $y = mx$, so the equation is $y = \frac{1}{4}x$. Of the given choices, only choice C (4, 1), satisfies this equation:

$$y = \frac{1}{4}x \rightarrow 1 = \frac{1}{4}(4) = 1$$

25) Choice C is correct
The area of the floor is: 8 cm × 22 cm = 176 cm^2

The number of tiles needed = 176 ÷ 11 = 16

26) Choice D is correct
Let's compare each fraction: $\frac{5}{13} < \frac{4}{7} < \frac{3}{5} < \frac{7}{9}$ Only choice D provides the right order.

27) Choice C is correct
Use the information provided in the question to draw the shape.

Use Pythagorean Theorem: $a^2 + b^2 = c^2$

$12^2 + 16^2 = c^2 \Rightarrow 144 + 256 = c^2 \Rightarrow 400 = c^2 \Rightarrow c = 20$

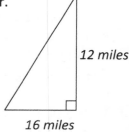

12 miles

16 miles

28) Choice A is correct
The ratio of boy to girls is 5:7. Therefore, there are 5 boys out of 12 students. To find the answer, first divide the total number of students by 12, then multiply the result by 5.

$60 \div 12 = 5 \Rightarrow 5 \times 5 = 25$. There are 25 boys and 35 (60-25) girls. So, 10 more boys should be enrolled to make the ratio 1:1

29) Choice A is correct
The question is this: 535.44 is what percent of 582? Use percent formula: part $= \frac{percent}{100} \times$ whole. $535.44 = \frac{percent}{100} \times 582 \Rightarrow 535.44 = \frac{percent \times 582}{100} \Rightarrow 53544 = percent \times 582 \Rightarrow percent = \frac{53544}{582} = 92$

53544 is 92 % of 582. Therefore, the discount is: 100% − 92% = 8%

30) Choice D is correct
If the score of Mia was 30, therefore the score of Ava is 60. Since, the score of Emma was half as that of Ava, therefore, the score of Emma is 120.

31) Choice D is correct
If 18 balls are removed from the bag at random, there will be one ball in the bag.

The probability of choosing a brown ball is 1 out of 19. Therefore, the probability of not choosing a red ball is 18 out of 19 and the probability of having not a red ball after removing 18 balls is the same.

32) Choice D is correct
Let x be the smallest number. Then, these are the numbers: $x, x + 1, x + 2, x + 3, x + 4$

average $= \frac{\text{sum of terms}}{\text{number of terms}} \Rightarrow 45 = \frac{x+(x+1)+(x+2)+(x+3)+(x+4)}{5} \Rightarrow 45 = \frac{5x+10}{5} \Rightarrow 225 = 5x + 10 \Rightarrow$

$215 = 5x \Rightarrow x = 43$

33) Choices D is correct
Some of prime numbers are: 2, 3, 5, 7, 11, 13. Find the product of two consecutive prime numbers: $2 \times 3 = 6$ (not in the options), $3 \times 5 = 15$ (bingo!), $5 \times 7 = 35$ (not in the options)

$7 \times 11 = 77$ (not in the options)

34) Choice C is correct
The slop of line A is: $m = \frac{y_2-y_1}{x_2-x_1} = \frac{8-2}{6-4} = \frac{6}{2} = 3$
Parallel lines have the same slope and only choice C ($y = 3x - 1$) has slope of 1.
35) Choice B is correct
15% of the volume of the solution is alcohol. Let x be the volume of the solution.

Then: $15\% \ of \ x = 36 \ ml \Rightarrow 0.15 \ x = 36 \Rightarrow x = 36 \div 0.15 = 240$

36) Choice B is correct
average $= \dfrac{\text{sum of terms}}{\text{number of terms}}$

The sum of the weight of all girls is: $24 \times 68 = 1632 \ kg$

The sum of the weight of all boys is: $16 \times 75 = 1200 \ kg$

The sum of the weight of all students is: $1632 + 1200 = 2832 \ kg$

average $= \dfrac{2832}{40} = 70.8$

37) Choice A is correct
Subtracting $2x$ and adding 6 to both sides of $3x - 6 \geq 2x - 8$ gives $x \geq -2$. Therefore, x is a solution to $3x - 6 \geq 2x - 8$ if and only if x is greater than or equal to -2 and x is NOT a

solution to $3x - 6 \geq 2x - 8$ if and only if x is less than -2. Of the choices given, only -3 is less than -2 and, therefore, cannot be a value of x.

38) Choice D is correct

Given the two equations, substitute the numerical value of a into the second equation to solve for x. $a = \sqrt{5}$, $6a = \sqrt{3x}$, Substituting the numerical value for a into the equation with is as follows. $6(\sqrt{5}) = \sqrt{3x}$, Now square both side of the equation. $(6\sqrt{5})^2 = (\sqrt{3x})^2$ Remember to square both terms within the parentheses. Also, recall that squaring a square root sign cancels them out. $6^2\sqrt{5}^2 = 3x$, $36(5) = 3x$, $180 = 3x$, $x = 60$

39) Choice A is correct

Formula for the Surface area of a cylinder is: $SA = 2\pi r^2 + 2\pi rh \rightarrow 130\pi = 2\pi r^2 + 2\pi r(8) \rightarrow r^2 + 8r - 65 = 0 \rightarrow (r + 13)(r - 5) = 0 \rightarrow r = 5 \; or \; r = -13 \; (unacceptable)$

40) Choice A is correct

Let x be the number of years. Therefore, $1,200 per year equals $1,200x$.

starting from $14,400 annual salary means you should add that amount to $1,200x$.

Income more than that is: I > $1200x + 14400$

41) Choice B is correct

A zero of a function corresponds to an x-intercept of the graph of the function in the xy-plane. Therefore, the graph of the function $g(x)$, which has four distinct zeros, must have four x-intercepts. Only the graph in choice C has four x-intercepts.

42) Choice D is correct

$0.3x = (0.45) \times 24 \rightarrow x = 36 \rightarrow (x - 6)^2 = (36 - 6)^2 = 30^2 = 900$

43) Choice C is correct

The weight of 14.6 meters of this rope is: $14.6 \times 600 \; g = 8,760 \; g$

1 kg = 1,000 g, therefore, $8,760 \; g \div 1000 = 8.76 \; kg$

44) Choice B is correct

$y = 5a^2b - 3ab^3$.   Plug in the values of a and b in the equation: a = 2 and b = -1
$y = 5(2)^2(-1) - 3(2)(-1)^3 = -5(4) + 6 = -20 + 6 = -14$

45) Choice C is correct

Use the information provided in the question to draw the shape.
Use Pythagorean Theorem: a² + b² = c²
$36^2 + 77^2 = c^2 \Rightarrow 1,296 + 5,929 = c^2 \Rightarrow 7,225 = c^2 \Rightarrow c = 85$

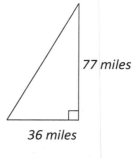

77 miles

36 miles

46) Choice C is correct

The four-term polynomial expression can be factored completely, by grouping, as follows: $(x^3 - 7x^2) + (4x - 28) = 0$
$x^2(x - 7) + 4(x - 7) = 0$ $(x - 7)(x^2 + 4) = 0$

By the zero-product property, set each factor of the polynomial equal to 0 and solve each resulting equation for x. This gives $x = 7$ or $x = \pm i\sqrt{4} = \pm i2$, respectively. Because the equation the question asks for the real value of x that satisfies the equation, the correct answer is 7.

47) Choice C is correct.

To solve for $f(7g(P))$, first, find $7g(p)$. $\quad g(x) = log_7x \rightarrow g(p) = log_7p \rightarrow 7g(p) = 7log_7p = log_7p^7 \Rightarrow$ Now, find $f(7g(p))$: $f(x) = 7^x \rightarrow f(log_7p^7) = 7^{log_7p^7}$

Logarithms and exponentials with the same base cancel each other. This is true because logarithms and exponentials are inverse operations. Then: $f(log_7p^7) = 7^{log_7p^7} = p^7$

48) Choice C is correct

0.98 per minute to use car. This per-minute rate can be converted to the hourly rate using the conversion 1 hour = 60 minutes, as shown below.

$$\frac{0.98}{minute} \times \frac{60 \; minutes}{1 \; hours} = \frac{\$(0.98 \times 60)}{hour}$$

Thus, the car costs $\$(0.98 \times 60)$ per hour. Therefore, the cost c, in dollars, for h hours of use is $c = (0.98 \times 60)h$, Which is equivalent to $c = 0.98(60h)$

49) Choice D is correct

The best way to deal with changing averages is to use the sum. Use the old average to figure out the total of the first 3 scores: Sum of first 3 scores: $(3)(90) = 270$

Use the new average to figure out the total she needs after the 4th score: Sum of 4 score: $(4)(92) = 368$, To get her sum from 270 to 368, Mary needs to score $368 - 270 = 98$.

50) Choice C is correct

To solve a quadratic equation, put it in the $ax^2 + bx + c = 0$ form, factor the left side, and set each factor equal to 0 separately to get the two solutions. To solve $x^2 = 24 - 5x$, first, rewrite it as $x^2 + 5x - 24 = 0$. Then factor the left side: $x^2 + 5x - 24 = 0$, $(x - 3)(x + 8) = 0$ $x = 3$ Or $x = -8$, There are two solutions for the equation.

51) Choice A is correct

Replace z by $z/3$ and simplify.

$$x_1 = \frac{8y + \dfrac{r}{r+1}}{\dfrac{z}{2}} = \frac{8y + \dfrac{r}{r+1}}{\dfrac{2 \times 6}{z}} = \frac{8y + \dfrac{r}{r+1}}{2 \times \dfrac{6}{z}} = \frac{1}{2} \times \frac{8y + \dfrac{r}{r+1}}{\dfrac{6}{z}} = \frac{x}{2}$$

52) Choice B is correct

$f(x) = x^3 - 4x^2 + 3x - 6$, $g(x) = 3$, then $f(g(x)) = f(3) = (3)^3 - 4(3)^2 + 3(3) - 6 = -6$

53) Choice A is correct.

Let the number be A. Then: $a = b\% \times A$. Solve for A. $a = \frac{b}{100} \times A$

Multiply both sides by $\frac{100}{b}$: $a \times \frac{100}{b} = \frac{b}{100} \times \frac{100}{b} \times A \rightarrow A = \frac{100a}{b}$

54) Choice D is correct

The line passes through the origin, $(7, m)$ and $(m, 14)$.

Any two of these points can be used to find the slope of the line. Since the line passes through $(0, 0)$ and $(7, m)$, the slope of the line is equal to $\frac{m - 0}{7 - 0} = \frac{m}{7}$. Similarly, since the line passes through $(0, 0)$ and $(m, 14)$, the slope of the line is equal to $\frac{14 - 0}{m - 0} = \frac{14}{m}$. Since each expression gives the slope of the same line, it must be true that $\frac{m}{7} = \frac{14}{m}$

Using cross multiplication gives

$\frac{m}{7} = \frac{14}{m} \rightarrow m^2 = 7 \times 14 = 98 \rightarrow m = \pm\sqrt{98} = \pm\sqrt{49 \times 2} = \pm\sqrt{49} \times \sqrt{2} = \pm 7\sqrt{2}$

55) Choice B is correct

It is given that $g(8) = 6$. Therefore, to find the value of $f(g(8))$, then $f(g(8)) = f(6) = 4$

56) Choice C is correct

Plug in each pair of number in the equation:

A. (-1, 2): $3(-1) - 2(2) = -7$ Nope!
B. (1, 3): $3(1) - 2(3) = -3$ Nope!
C. (2, -3): $3(2) - 2(-3) = 12$ Bingo!
D. (2, 2): $3(2) - 2(2) = 2$ Nope!

57) Choice B is correct

Here we can substitute 7 for x in the equation. Thus, $3y + 3 = 6(7 - 4)$, $\rightarrow 3y + 3 = 18$
Subtracting 3 to both side of the equation: $3y = 18 - 3 = 15, \rightarrow 3y = 15$ $\rightarrow$ divide two sides by 3, $y = 5$

58) Choice A is correct

Let's review the options: I. $|a| < 1 \rightarrow -1 < a < 1$
Multiply all sides by b. Since, $b > 0 \rightarrow -b < ba < b$

II. Since, $-1 < a < 1, and \ a < 0 \rightarrow -a > a^2 > a$ (plug in $-\frac{1}{2}$, and check!)

III. $-1 < a < 1, multiply \ all \ sides \ by \ 4, then:$
$-4 < 4a < 4, sutract \ 3 \ from \ all \ sides, then:$
$$-4 - 3 < 4a - 3 < 4 - 3 \rightarrow -7 < 4a - 3 < 1$$

I only incorrect.

59) Choice C is correct

The equation can be rewritten as

$c - d = ac \rightarrow (divide \ both \ sides \ by \ c) \ 1 - \frac{d}{c} = a$, since $c < 0$ and $d > 0$, the value of $-\frac{d}{c}$
is positive. Therefore, 1 plus a positive number is positive. a must be greater than 1. $a > 1$

60) Choice D is correct

$f(x) = 2x^2 - 5x + 1, g(x) = -3x^2 - 6x + 4$
$(f - g)(x) = f(x) - g(x) = (2x^2 - 5x + 1) - (-3x^2 - 6x + 4) = (2x^2 + 3x^2) + (-5x + 6x) + (1 - 4) = 5x^2 + x - 3$

CLEP College Mathematics Practice Test 2

1) Choice D is correct

To find the number of possible outfit combinations, multiply number of options for each factor:
$4 \times 2 \times 3 = 24$

2) Choice B is correct

Simplify and combine like terms. $(8x^4 - 3x^3 + 6x^2) - (5x^4 + 7x^2 - 5x) \Rightarrow$

$(8x^4 - 3x^3 + 6x^2) - 5x^4 - 7x^2 + 5x = 3x^4 - 3x^3 - x^2 + 5x$

3) Choice B is correct

The population is increased by 12% and 10%. 12% increase changes the population to 112% of original population. For the second increase, multiply the result by 110%. $(1.12) \times (1.10) = 1.23 = 123\% \Rightarrow$ 23 percent of the population is increased after two years.

4) Choice C is correct

Solve for x. $1 \leq 2x - 5 < 11 \Rightarrow$ (add 5 all sides) $1 + 5 \leq 2x - 5 + 5 < 11 + 5 \Rightarrow 6 \leq 2x < 16$ $\Rightarrow$ (divide all sides by 2) $3 \leq x < 8$, x is between 3 and 8. Choice C represent this inequality.

5) Choice D is correct

$Volume\ of\ a\ box = length \times width \times height = 5 \times 4 \times 8 = 160$

6) Choice B is correct

Adding 9 to each side of the inequality $3n - 7 \geq 1$ yields the inequality $3n + 2 \geq 10$. Therefore, the least possible value of $3n + 2$ is 10.

7) Choice B is correct

To get a sum of 5 for two dice, we can get 4 different options: (1, 4), (4,1), (2, 3), (3, 2)

To get a sum of 3 for two dice, we can get 2 different options: (1, 2), (2, 1)

Therefore, there are 6 options to get the sum of 3 or 5. Since, we have 6 × 6 = 36 total options, the probability of getting a sum of 3 and 5 is 6 out of 36 or $\frac{1}{6}$.

8) Choice C is correct

Four times of 36,000 is 144,000. One sixth of them cancelled their tickets.

One sixth of 144,000 equals 24,000 ($\frac{1}{6} \times 144000 = 24000$).

$120,000 (144,000 - 24,000 = 120,000)$ fans are attending this week

9) Choice B is correct

The area of the square is 1,024. Therefore, the side of the square is square root of the area. $\sqrt{1024} = 32$

Four times the side of the square is the perimeter: $4 \times 32 = 128$

10) Choice C is correct

$2x - y = 5$. Plug in the values of x and y from choices provided. Then:

A. $(-1, 4)$ $2x - y = 5 \rightarrow 2(-1) - 4 = -6$ This is NOT true!

B. $(2, -3)$ $2x - y = 5 \rightarrow 2(2) - (-3) = 7$ This is NOT true!

C. $(3, 1)$ $2x - y = 5 \rightarrow 2(3) - 1 = 5$ This is true!

D. $(4, 2)$ $2x - y = 5 \rightarrow 2(4) - 2 = 6$ This is NOT true!

11) Choice C is correct

The width of the rectangle is twice its length. Let x be the length. Then, $width = \frac{x}{6}$

Perimeter of the rectangle is 2 (width + length) = $2\left(\frac{x}{6} + x\right) = 70 \Rightarrow 2(\frac{7}{6}x) = 70 \Rightarrow x = 30$

Length of the rectangle is 30 meters.

12) Choice B is correct

Change the numbers to decimal and then compare. $\frac{2}{5} = 0.4$, $85\% = 0.85$, $\frac{7}{9} = 0.77$, $\frac{3}{4} = 0.75$

Then: $\frac{2}{5} < \frac{3}{4} < \frac{7}{9} < 85\%$

13) Choice D is correct

average (mean) $= \frac{\text{sum of terms}}{\text{number of terms}} \Rightarrow 94 = \frac{\text{sum of terms}}{25} \Rightarrow sum = 94 \times 25 = 2350$

The difference of 86 and 68 is 18. Therefore, 18 should be subtracted from the sum.

$2350 - 18 = 2332, \quad \text{mean} = \frac{\text{sum of terms}}{\text{number of terms}} \Rightarrow \text{mean} = \frac{2332}{25} = 93.28$

14) Choice D is correct

In the stadium the ratio of home fans to visiting fans in a crowd is 5:8. Therefore, total number of fans must be divisible by 13: 5 + 8 = 13.
Let's review the choices:
A. 9,862: $9,862 \div 13 = 758.61$

B. 11,480: $11,480 \div 13 = 883,07$

C. 23,577: $23,577 \div 13 = 1813.61$

D. 32,227: $32,227 \div 13 = 2479$

Only choice D when divided by 13 results a whole number.

15) Choice B is correct

The probability of choosing a Hearts is $\frac{13}{52} = \frac{1}{4}$

16) Choice B is correct

The diagonal of the square is 6. Let x be the side.

Use Pythagorean Theorem: $a^2 + b^2 = c^2$

$x^2 + x^2 = 6^2 \Rightarrow 2x^2 = 6^2 \Rightarrow 2x^2 = 36 \Rightarrow x^2 = 18 \Rightarrow x = \sqrt{18}$

The area of the square is: $\sqrt{18} \times \sqrt{18} = 18$

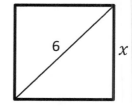

17) Choice C is correct

$$\text{Probability} = \frac{number\ of\ desired\ outcomes}{number\ of\ total\ outcomes} = \frac{16}{15+16+22+15} = \frac{16}{68} = \frac{4}{17}$$

18) Choice A is correct

average $= \dfrac{\text{sum of terms}}{\text{number of terms}} \Rightarrow$ (average of 8 numbers) $18 = \dfrac{\text{sum of numbers}}{8} \Rightarrow$ sum of 8 numbers is $18 \times 8 = 144$

(average of 6 numbers) $16 = \dfrac{\text{sum of numbers}}{6} \Rightarrow$ sum of 6 numbers is $16 \times 6 = 96 \Rightarrow$ sum of 8

numbers − sum of 6 numbers = sum of 2 numbers $144-96=48$, average of 2 numbers $= \dfrac{48}{2} = 24$

19) Choice C is correct

Solving Systems of Equations by Elimination

Multiply the first equation by (−2), then add it to the second equation.

$\begin{array}{l} -2(x+y= \ 5) \\ \underline{\ \ 2x+y=7\ \ } \end{array} \Rightarrow \begin{array}{l} -2x-2y=-10 \\ \ \ 2x+y=7 \end{array} \Rightarrow -y=-3 \Rightarrow y= \ 3$

Plug in the value of y into one of the equations and solve for x. $x+3=5 \Rightarrow x=2$

20) Choice C is correct

The perimeter of the trapezoid is 50 cm.
Therefore, the missing side (height) is $50-(8+16+12)=50-36=14$. Area of a
trapezoid: $A= \frac{1}{2}h\ (b_1+b_2)= \frac{1}{2}(14)(8+12)=140$

21) Choice C is correct

First, find the number. Let x be the number. Write the equation and solve for x.

120 % of a number is 84, then: $1.2 \times x = 84 \Rightarrow x = 84 \div 1.2 = 70$

85 % of 70 is: $0.85 \times 70 = 59.5$

22) Choice A is correct

$f(x)=5x^2-2x, g(x)=6x-4, (\frac{f}{g})(x)=\dfrac{f(x)}{g(x)}=\dfrac{5x^2-2x}{6x-4}$

23) Choice A is correct

Use formula of rectangle prism volume. $V=(length)(width)(height) \Rightarrow 4,410=(35)(14)(height) \Rightarrow height=4,410 \div 490=9$

24) Choice D is correct

The square of a number is $\frac{49}{81}$, then the number is the square root of $\frac{49}{81}$ $\sqrt{\frac{49}{81}}=\frac{7}{9}$

The cube of the number is: $(\frac{7}{9})^3=\frac{343}{729}$

25) Choice C is correct

Let L be the length of the rectangular and W be the with of the rectangular. Then, $L = 2W + 4$

The perimeter of the rectangle is 32 meters. Therefore: $2L + 2W = 32$ $L + W = 16$

Replace the value of L from the first equation into the second equation and solve for W:

$$(2W + 4) + W = 16 \rightarrow 3W + 4 = 16 \rightarrow 3W = 12 \rightarrow W = 4$$

The width of the rectangle is 4 meters and its length is: $L = 2W + 4 = 2(4) + 4 = 12$

The area of the rectangle is: length × width = 4 × 12 = 48

26) Choice C is correct

$b^{\frac{m}{n}} = \sqrt[n]{b^m}$ For any positive integers m and n. Thus, $b^{\frac{3}{4}} = \sqrt[4]{b^3}$.

27) Choice A is correct

3,200 out of 96,000 equals to $\dfrac{3200}{96000} = \dfrac{4}{120} = \dfrac{1}{30}$

28) Choice A is correct

Jason needs an 85% average to pass for six exams. Therefore, the sum of 6 exams must be at lease $85 \times 6 = 510$. The sum of 5 exams is: $92 + 83 + 75 + 89 + 76 = 415$

The minimum score Jason can earn on his 6th and final test to pass is: $510 - 415 = 95$

29) Choice D is correct

Isolate and solve for x. $\dfrac{3}{8}x + \dfrac{5}{24} = \dfrac{3}{4} \Rightarrow \dfrac{3}{8}x = \dfrac{3}{4} - \dfrac{5}{24} = \dfrac{18-5}{24} = \dfrac{13}{24} \Rightarrow \dfrac{3}{8}x = \dfrac{13}{24}$

Multiply both sides by the reciprocal of the coefficient of x. $(\dfrac{8}{3}) \dfrac{3}{8}x = \dfrac{13}{24} (\dfrac{8}{3}) \Rightarrow x = \dfrac{13}{9}$

30) Choice D is correct

Surface Area of a cylinder = 2πr (r + h), The radius of the cylinder is 4, (8 ÷ 2) inches and its height is 12 inches. Therefore, Surface Area of a cylinder = 2π (4) (4 + 12) = 128 π

31) Choice D is correct

First, find the sum of five numbers.

average = $\dfrac{\text{sum of terms}}{\text{number of terms}} \Rightarrow 24 = \dfrac{\text{sum of 5 numbers}}{5} \Rightarrow$ sum of 5 numbers = 24 × 5 = 120

The sum of 5 numbers is 120. If a sixth number that is greater than 42 is added to these numbers, then the sum of 6 numbers must be greater than 162.   120 + 42 = 162

If the number was 42, then the average of the numbers is:

average = $\dfrac{\text{sum of terms}}{\text{number of terms}} = \dfrac{162}{6} = 27$

Since the number is bigger than 42. Then, the average of six numbers must be greater than 27. Choice D is greater than 27.

32) Choice B is correct

Use simple interest formula: $I = prt$ (I = interest, p = principal, r = rate, t = time)

$$I = (15000)(0.045)(6) = 4050$$

33) Choice C is correct

Use Pythagorean Theorem: $a^2 + b^2 = c^2$ $5^2 + 12^2 = c^2 \Rightarrow 169 = c^2 \Rightarrow c = 13$

34) Choice C is correct

Plug in 122 for F and then solve for C. $C = \frac{5}{9}(F - 32) \Rightarrow C = \frac{5}{9}(122 - 32) \Rightarrow C = \frac{5}{9}(90) = 50$

35) Choice B is correct

Let x be the number. Write the equation and solve for x.

60% of $x = 3 \Rightarrow 0.60\, x = 3 \Rightarrow x = 3 \div 0.60 = 5$

36) Choice D is correct

Let x be all expenses, then $\frac{25}{100}x = \$840 \rightarrow x = \frac{100 \times \$840}{25} = \$3{,}360$

He spent for his rent: $\frac{16}{100} \times \$3{,}360 = \$537.6$

37) Choice C is correct

The distance between Jason and Joe is 12 miles. Jason running at 6.5 miles per hour and Joe is running at the speed of 8 miles per hour. Therefore, every hour the distance is 1.5 miles less. $12 \div 1.5 = 8$

38) Choice D is correct

The failing rate is 18 out of 72 $= \frac{18}{72}$.   Change the fraction to percent: $\frac{18}{72} \times 100\% = 25\%$

25 percent of students failed. Therefore, 75 percent of students passed the exam.

39) Choice C is correct

Write the numbers in order: 6, 13, 28, 32, 57, 61, 79

Median is the number in the middle. So, the median is 32.

40) Choice D is correct

Let's find the vertex of each choice provided:
A. $y = 2x^2 - 2$ The vertex is: $(0, -2)$
B. $y = -2x^2 + 2$ The vertex is: $(0, 2)$
C. $y = x^2 + 2x - 2$

The value of x of the vertex in the equation of a quadratic in standard form is: $x = \frac{-b}{2a} = \frac{-2}{2} = -1$

(The standard equation of a quadratic is: $ax^2 + bx + c = 0$)

The value of x in the vertex is -1 not 2.

D. $y = 3(x-2)^2 + 2$

Vertex form of a parabola equation is in form of $y = a(x-h)^2 + k$, where (h, k) is the vertex. Then $h = 2$ and $k = -2$. (This is the answer)

41) Choice B is correct

Plugin the values of x in the choices provided. The points are $(1, 3), (2, 5), and\ (3, 7)$

For $(1, 3)$ check the options provided:

A. $g(x) = x + 1 \rightarrow 3 = 1 + 1 \rightarrow 2 = 3$ *This is NOT true.*

B. $g(x) = 2x + 1 \rightarrow 3 = 2(1) + 1 \rightarrow 3 = 3$ *This is true.*

C. $g(x) = 2x - 1 \rightarrow 3 = 2(1) - 1 \rightarrow 1 = 3$ *This is NOT true.*

D. $g(x) = x^2 + 1 \rightarrow 3 = (1)^2 + 1 \rightarrow 2 = 3$ *This is NOT true.*

From the choices provided, only choice B is correct.

42) Choice C is correct.

Simplify the expression. $\sqrt{\frac{x^2}{8} + \frac{x^2}{16}} = \sqrt{\frac{2x^2}{16} + \frac{x^2}{16}} = \sqrt{\frac{3x^2}{16}} = \sqrt{\frac{3}{16}x^2} = \sqrt{\frac{3}{16}} \times \sqrt{x^2} = \frac{\sqrt{3}}{4} \times x = \frac{\sqrt{3}}{4}x$

43) Choice B is correct

To find the $y-$intercept of a line from its equation, put the equation in slope-intercept form:

$4x - 3y = 18, \ -3y = 18 - 4x, \ \ \ 3y = 4x - 18, \ y = \frac{4}{3}x - 6$

The $y-$intercept is what comes after the x. Thus, the $y-$intercept of the line is -6.

44) Choice D is correct

Adding both side of $6a - 9 = 33$ by 9 gives $6a = 42$

Divide both side of $6a = 42$ by 6 gives $a = 7$, then $3a = 3(7) = 21$

45) Choice B is correct

The easiest way to solve this one is to plug the answers into the equation.

When you do this, you will see the only time $x = x^{-6}$ is when $x = 1$ or $x = 0$.

Only $x = 1$ is provided in the choices.

46) Choice D is correct

First find a common denominator for both of the fractions in the expression $\frac{3}{2x} - \frac{5x-8}{6x^2}$.

of $3x$, we can combine like terms into a single numerator over the denominator:

$$\frac{9x}{6x^2} - \frac{5x-8}{6x^2} = \frac{9x - (5x-8)}{6x^2} = \frac{4x+8}{6x^2} = \frac{2x+4}{3x^2}$$

47) Choice D is correct

Simplify. $3x^2y^2(4xy^3)^2 = 3x^2y^2(16x^2y^6) = 48x^4y^8$

48) Choice D is correct

To find the average of three numbers even if they're algebraic expressions, add them up and divide by 3. Thus, the average equals: $\frac{(3x-5)+(4x+2)+(5x+6)}{3} = \frac{12x+3}{3} = \frac{3(4x+1)}{3} = 4x + 1$

49) Choice C is correct

The equation of a line in slope intercept form is: $y = mx + b$. Solve for y. $3x - 6y = 15 \Rightarrow -6y = 15 - 3x \Rightarrow 6y = 3x - 15 \Rightarrow y = \frac{1}{2}x - \frac{15}{6}$. The slope is $\frac{1}{2}$. The slope of the line perpendicular to this line is: $m_1 \times m_2 = -1 \Rightarrow \frac{1}{2} \times m_2 = -1 \Rightarrow m_2 = -2$

50) Choice C is correct

Write the ratio of $7a$ to $3b$. $\frac{7a}{3b} = \frac{1}{12}$

Use cross multiplication and then simplify. $7a \times 12 = 3b \times 1 \rightarrow 84a = 3b \rightarrow a = \frac{3b}{84} = \frac{b}{28}$

Now, find the ratio of a to b. $\frac{a}{b} = \frac{\frac{b}{28}}{b} \rightarrow \frac{b}{28} \div b = \frac{b}{28} \times \frac{1}{b} = \frac{b}{28b} = \frac{1}{28}$

51) Choice D is correct

The area of rectangle is: $8 \times 6 = 48$ cm². The area of circle is: $\pi r^2 = \pi \times (\frac{12}{2})^2 = 3 \times 36 = 108$ cm². Difference of areas is: $108 - 48 = 60$

52) Choice A is correct

$f(x) = x^3 - 2x^2 + 7x, g(x) = 2x, f(g(x)) = (2x)^3 - 2(2x)^2 + 7(2x) = 8x^3 - 8x^2 + 14x$

53) Choice B is correct

$1,024 = 4^5 \rightarrow 4^x = 4^5 \rightarrow x = 5$

54) Choice A is correct

Use the information provided in the question to draw the shape.
Use Pythagorean Theorem: $a^2 + b^2 = c^2$
$20^2 + 21^2 = c^2 \Rightarrow 400 + 441 = c^2 \Rightarrow 841 = c^2 \Rightarrow c = 29$

Port A

21 miles

20 miles

55) Choice D is correct.

Let L be the length of the rectangular and W be the with of the rectangular. Then, $L = 3W + 6$
The perimeter of the rectangle is 44 meters. Therefore: $2L + 2W = 44 \qquad L + W = 22$
Replace the value of L from the first equation into the second equation and solve for W:
$$(3W + 6) + W = 22 \rightarrow 4W + 6 = 22 \rightarrow 4W = 16 \rightarrow W = 4$$
The width of the rectangle is 4 meters and its length is: $L = 3W + 6 = 3(4) + 6 = 18$
The area of the rectangle is: length × width = 4 × 18 = 72

56) Choice C is correct.

Let x be the number of adult tickets and y be the number of student tickets. Then:
$x + y = 15, \quad 12x + 8y = 140$
Use elimination method to solve this system of equation. Multiply the first equation by -8 and add it to the second equation. $-8(x + y = 15), -8x - 8y = -120, 12x + 8y = 140$
$\quad 4x = 20, \quad x = 8$
There are 5 adult tickets and 10 student tickets.

57) Choice C is correct

Since the triangle ABC is reflected over the y-axis, then all values of y's of the points don't change and the sign of all x's change. (remember that when a point is reflected over the y-axis, the value of y does not change and when a point is reflected over the x-axis, the value of x does not change). Therefore: (3, -2) changes to (-3, -2). (5, 1) changes to (-5, 1). (-2, 3) changes to (2, 3)

58) Choice B is correct

Plug in the value of x in the equation and solve for y.

$$4y = \frac{5x^2}{9} - 3 \rightarrow 4y = \frac{5(3)^2}{9} - 3 \rightarrow 4y = \frac{5(9)}{9} - 3 \rightarrow 4y = 5 - 3 = 2 \rightarrow 4y = 2, y = \frac{1}{2}$$

59) Choice A is correct

Since a box of pen costs \$2, then $2p$ Represents the cost of p boxes of pen.

Multiplying this number times 1.065 will increase the cost by the 6.5% for tax.

Then add the \$8 shipping fee for the total: $1.065(2p) + 8$

60) Choice D is correct

Rate of change (growth or x) is 6 per week. $54 \div 6 = 9$

Since the plant grows at a linear rate, then the relationship between the height (y) of the plant and number of weeks of growth (x) can be written as: $y(x) = 9x$

www.EffortlessMath.com

... So Much More Online!

✓ FREE Math lessons

✓ More Math learning books!

✓ Mathematics Worksheets

✓ Online Math Tutors

Need a PDF version of this book?

Please visit www.EffortlessMath.com

CPSIA information can be obtained
at www.ICGtesting.com
Printed in the USA
BVHW011113070920
588225BV00015B/947